TRAPPED

Trapped

Published by The Conrad Press in the United Kingdom 2019

Tel: +44(0)1227 472 874
www.theconradpress.com
info@theconradpress.com

ISBN 978-1-911546-40-5

Typesetting and Cover Design by:
Charlotte Mouncey, www.bookstyle.co.uk

The Conrad Press logo was designed by Maria Priestley.

Printed and bound in Great Britain
by Clays Ltd, Elcograf S.p.A.

TRAPPED

A NOVEL ABOUT THE LOST 1845 FRANKLIN EXPEDITION TO SEEK A NORTH-WEST PASSAGE

JOHN ROOBOL

Prologue

It is late in the morning of Tuesday, May the nineteenth 1846.

Two three-masted wooden sailing ships are frozen into the ice in a winter harbour behind the flat-topped six-hundred-foot-high Beechey Island, in Barrow Strait, in what is today the Canadian Arctic.

The hills are blanketed white with winter snow that is drifting in a strong cold wind.

In the great cabin of the flagship a portly, bald-headed old captain is writing at a long table by lantern light with a quill pen.

He wears glasses on his round, kindly face, that shows lines of tiredness. He is dressed in the royal navy uniform of a captain with a royal-blue double-breasted coat with sixteen gold buttons and scarlet facings and cuffs, and royal blue gold-striped trousers.

On his shoulders he wears gold-fringed epaulettes embossed with a crown and single anchor on each shoulder. He is Sir John Franklin, leader of a Royal Navy Expedition to complete the mapping of the North-West Passage - a sea route between Europe and Asia around the north of the American continent - and if possible to sail home through it. For centuries, European explorers sought a navigable passage as a possible trade route to Asia. The economic and mercantile benefits to the nation that discovered a navigable North-West Passage would be immense. The old captain puts down the quill, raises his glasses onto his forehead, rubs his eyes and stretches his arms. He looks around the cabin, firstly at the two portraits hanging above the stern windows. One shows Queen Victoria and the other his second wife, Lady Jane Franklin. He sighs and remembers the rose fragrance Jane habitually wore and sadly wonders if he will ever see her again and enjoy that fragrance once more.

Franklin then turns back to the pages he has written and smiles at the memories of the year. Yes, it has been a great success. One year ago to this day the two expedition ships H.M.S. Erebus and H.M.S. Terror set sail.

They had left Greenhithe on Monday May the nineteenth 1845. A supply ship - the Baretto Junior - had accompanied them as far as Disko Island in Greenland. There they had spent eight days topping up their supplies. The two expedition ships then crossed Baffin Bay and entered Lancaster Sound – the eastern gateway of the North-West Passage.

Franklin remembered the conversation on entering Lancaster Sound - the eastern end of the North-West Passage. He had been on deck with Commander Fitzjames and Lieutenant Gore and had addressed them. The two officers were Franklin's right-hand men aboard the flagship. Commander James Fitzjames was second-in-command and Graham Gore was First Lieutenant. They were similar men in many respects and in a sense typical of the navy's finest officers selected for the expedition.

Both were in their thirties, Fitzjames was thirty-four and Gore a few years older. Both were fit, strong, confident men with distinguished service records including battle experience. Fitzjames was the bigger and heavier of the two. He had a confident buoyant personality and was popular with his fellow officers. He spoke with an upper-class accent and a slight lisp. Gore was also popular and liked to paint sketches and play the flute.

'So, we're now in the middle of the Croker Mountains,' Franklin observed. He smiled faintly. 'Back in 1818, Sir John Ross thought he saw a mountain range blocking this sound, and mapped it as a bay. It's an easy thing to do in the Arctic because of the mist and the strange lighting effects on cloud and ice. He named the mountain range after the First Secretary of the Admiralty. The next year, Edward Parry returned and sailed right through the so-called Croker Mountains – a remarkably insubstantial mountain range. He then sailed on westwards for another 620 miles to winter at Melville Island.'

Commander Fitzjames nodded: 'An heroic and lucrative discovery, sir. As I recall, he did so well he was awarded £5,000 for crossing the 110th meridian.'

'Yes,' agreed Sir John. 'If we can get through the North-West Passage then we'll be eligible for the Admiralty reward of £20,000. That would be an even more heroic and lucrative achievement. Well, gentlemen, at least we can learn from Sir William Parry's efforts. He tried to sail west to get to Bering Strait, but was stopped by a great river of ice.'

Fitzjames gave a gruff nod: 'Well, that's at least one route less that we won't have to search.'

'Yes, indeed,' said Franklin. 'We should drink a toast to Sir Edward this evening.'

And indeed they did.

The ships continued westwards into Barrow Strait. One morning, a week or so after that conversation, Franklin and Fitzjames were on the quarter deck admiring the splendid scenery. Snow-covered mountains at the east end of Devon

Island rose to what they estimated as about 6,500 feet and the sea was filled with pieces of ice all drifting to the east.

'I believe the source of this ice is the great ice river that stopped Parry at Melville Island,' Franklin said. 'It flows south-east past Melville Island from a source in the Polar Sea.'

'There seems to be a great deal of it.'

'Oh, there is a lot more than this. In 1830 Ross saw such an ice river on the west side of Cape Felix in King William Land. He reported that the ice blocks were pushed up onto the shore for up to a half mile inland.'

'Yes, Sir John, the Ross book and others by previous polar explorers in the ship's library have been in constant circulation since we left Greenland.'

With north-westerly winds, they had found and used the ice-free water between Devon Island and the icy central parts of Lancaster Sound and Barrow Strait. As they sailed west the land fell gradually until they reached Wellington Channel. There on the east side of the entrance to the channel they saw the excellent sheltered harbour behind Beechey Island, first noted by Parry. This appeared to be an ideal place to spend their first winter in the ice.

Wellington Channel appeared to be open, as the north-westerly winds had driven the ice away from the west side, leaving open water. Their orders from the Admiralty were to explore Wellington Channel if ice prevented them from proceeding south-west after Cape Walker. Franklin had decided to continue to Cape Walker.

But before they reached it (where their Admiralty orders were for them to start their exploration) Ice Master Reid, in the crow's nest with his telescope, called down that he could see what appeared to be an open bay or sound immediately to the east of Cape Walker. But Sir John decided to stick with his orders and to pass Cape Walker before turning south-west.

So they had passed Cape Walker, but found the strait ahead to be closed with much ice that was moving. There were no open routes to the south or south west either. Again Ice Master Reid with his telescope called down to report that he could see the ice river moving not only eastwards towards them, but also great blocks of ice turning over and there was a low rumbling noise. They better understood now what had stopped Parry. Indeed they were somewhat dismayed, for their orders were to proceed to the south-west, but the moving ice river made this impossible.

Franklin went to speak to Fitzjames. 'Commander, we have our orders very clearly to proceed south-west from here but there are no open passages. We must go back.'

'Yes, but don't you think we've a great opportunity to try to follow the open water we saw in Wellington Channel? This option is in accordance with the Admiralty Instructions and it would also enable us to test the idea of an open Polar Sea.'

Franklin gave a shrug and agreed. Fitzjames was delighted.

'I've long been interested in the possibility of an open Polar Sea, Sir John.'

So flags were hoisted and the ships came about and it was not too long before they found ourselves sailing north into Wellington Channel in completely unexplored waters.

The channel is about fifty miles wide with low-lying land up to 300 feet high on either side. The rocks on both sides of the channel could be seen to be stratified or layered sedimentary in nature. To the west lay Cornwallis Land and to the east Devon Island. Except perhaps for Eskimos, they were the first men ever to reach the north coast of Cornwallis Land at latitude seventy-five degrees and thirty-eight minutes, after sailing fifty-four miles north.

The channel continued north, now between Bathurst and Devon Islands and they proceeded further north for another 110 miles. They finally emerged between the northern headlands of Bathurst and Devon Islands to view ahead of them the huge expanse of the great Polar Sea. But they could see also some snowy peaks indicating that Arctic Islands continued further north. They saw that the great Polar Sea was entirely covered in ice. Franklin, viewing all this from the quarter deck where he stood next to Fitzjames, exclaimed:

'So there it is James, the Polar Sea and it's all ice.'

'What a dreadful shame,' said Fitzjames. 'Like Sir John Barrow, I've long believed ice to accumulate around the land and islands here and that an open Polar Sea existed.'

Franklin nodded: 'Yes, it disappoints me too, because had there been an open Polar Sea, then it might have provided us with a North-West Passage to Bering Strait and home.'

'Interesting, but if there is no open Polar Sea, I wonder what the explanation is of how Atlantic whales have been taken that have stuck in their blubber stone spear heads from Russia, and other whales caught in Bering Strait have tips of iron harpoons in them that must have originated in Greenland.'

Franklin shrugged. 'I can't answer that. Perhaps our natural scientists might come up with an explanation at some point.'

The ships reached the edge of the ice at seventy-seven degrees north, and here Franklin ordered that they turn south and work their way along the north side of Cornwallis, which now appeared to be an island.

In order to prove this they worked the ships down a channel on the west side between Cornwallis and Bathurst Islands. This proved slow going and extremely hard work. The channel narrowed in places with small islands where ice accumulated. The specially strengthened bows of both ships served them well, as did the steam engines, although they had a habit of breaking down when most needed. There was very much work for the crews in some places cutting a channel through the ice using the ice saws. The ships were also moved by ice anchors, with the men hauling on the capstan. All the crew joined in, as the short summer was fast passing.

Eventually, with exhausted crews, they regained Barrow Strait and headed east to complete their circumnavigation of Cornwallis Island. They had proved that Cornwallis is not a part of Bathurst Island. That done, they next sought out the winter harbour behind Beechey Island in the shelter of Devon Island at the east side of the entrance to Wellington Channel.

The ships anchored at latitude seventy-four degrees forty-three minutes north in a winter harbour behind Beechey Island. Here they would winter for the next ten months.

They were over 200 miles north of the Arctic Circle, and in a place that was a snowy desert, even in summer. Yet the expedition was better equipped than previous polar expeditions and the ships were supplied for three years. Each had a former railway steam-engine of twenty horse-power to drive a retractable propeller. Each ship had a supply of ninety tons of coal. The latter was also used for cooking aboard the ship's Fraser Patent stoves. Hot water from the stoves was circulated by pipe around the lower deck of each ship where everyone lived.

The ships carried a vast amount of provisions, carefully calculated to provide for 137 men for 1,159 days or three years and two months. There were biscuits, flour, pemmican, salted beef, salt pork, preserved meat, sugar, preserved vegetables, concentrated spirits, wine for the sick, suet, raisins, peas, preserved vegetables, concentrated soup, vinegar, Scotch barley oatmeal, pickles, cranberries, mustard and pepper. The preserved meat, vegetables and concentrated soups were provided in tin cans, a relatively new invention. The expedition also carried 9,300 pounds of lemon juice, enough for each man to be issued with a daily ration of one ounce. In addition they carried 7,088 pounds of tobacco, 3,600 pounds of soap and 2,700 pounds of candles.

As things worked out, only 129 men left Greenland and entered the ice, so the stores should have been sufficient for 1,231 days or three years, four and a half months. A typical daily diet for the crew would have been one pound of biscuit or flour, three quarters of a pound of either salted beef or salted pork or a half pound of preserved meat, two and a half ounces of sugar, a quarter of an ounce of tea, one ounce of chocolate and one ounce of lemon juice. The officers had better and more varied food.

Sir John's thoughts were interrupted by a knock on the cabin door. He called out 'Enter'.

Commander James Fitzjames entered: 'Good morning, Sir John.'

'Good morning, Commander.'

'Sir John, the ship is in good order and I've just returned from making an inspection of the shore base.'

'How was the weather and what did you find?'

'Quite breezy, with snow being picked up. A lot of meltwater on top of the sea ice too. I got wet up to the knees again. But the store house and stores remain dry. The blacksmith's shop was busy making new fittings for some of the spars. The carpenter's workshop was buzzing with activity with both Erebus and Terror carpenters and their assistants working on the boats. They are mainly recaulking and repainting them. I checked the camp site and washing area too. There are men washing clothes in tubs today using melt-water heated in a cauldron over a waste wood fire. Some of the men prefer life ashore and find the ships confining.'

'Thank you, James. I have been writing up a diary of the expedition. Do you realise that today is the first anniversary since our expedition set out?'

'I'd forgotten that,' replied Fitzjames. 'We've completed our first Arctic winter snug and safe in a fine winter harbour and will soon have the ships ready to break out in July with the summer thaw. Things are going very well indeed'.

'And how are things with the magnetic stations, James?'

'All is well, Sir John. Lieutenant Fairholme and two seamen are at the Beechey Island station. Lieutenant Le Vesconte and two other seamen are at present at the Cape Riley station.'

'Good and how about the scientific collections?'

'We are just setting up two additional camps for that work as well as for hunting. One is near a large limestone mass called Caswell's Tower, a few miles away. The other is about nine miles from Beechey Island up Wellington Channel and about six miles from Cape Spencer.'

'Good. My report is coming along well.'

'It's a harsh place and we did lose three men this winter.'

'Yes, that was most unfortunate. It had been my hope to return the expedition to England without casualties.'

'But the deaths were unavoidable. Surgeon Stanley identified the cause of death in all three cases to be consumption contracted before they left England. The extreme cold here worsened the condition.'

'Yes, but we'll leave a graveyard here The surgeons did send several men home from Greenland with suspected tuberculosis, but unfortunately those three slipped through their scrutiny.'

Commander Fitzjames then saluted and left the cabin. A steward knocked and brought in Sir John's lunch: 'Here you are Sir. Your favourite, a bowl of hot Irish stew with some hot bread and a mug of tea. The bread was fresh baked this morning.'

The old captain sat back in his chair and as he ate his lunch he remembered when the winter darkness had descended on the expedition and the men were largely confined to the ships and the immediate area of the shore camp.

One of the few pleasures was the periodic display of the aurora borealis. Many would turn out to watch the displays as long curtains of yellow, green, white and pink light shimmered and danced across the night sky. He had watched with Lieutenant Graham Gore one calm night on the ice alongside the ship. Lieutenant Gore had said:

'Sir John, have you heard anything about whether the aurora borealis is silent? Some claim to hear a low rustling or crackling sound. I think we should be able to decide what is right if we listen carefully.'

Franklin gave a nod and said, 'So far I've heard nothing but the sound now and again of wind, but I can you tell one thing, standing around here is making me powerfully cold. Shall we resume this exercise another night? I'm sure the other officers can give us their opinions too.'

It was the start of an exercise in which the officers divided into two groups. The majority settled for a silent phenomenon, but some, perhaps with better hearing, claimed to hear rustling noises.

An activity that kept most of the Lieutenants busy in the winter darkness was teaching the classes on both ships the 'Three Rs'– reading, writing and arithmetic. These were conducted for those members of the crew who wanted to learn and were well attended. The many slates and chalk, that had been brought along for just this purpose were in heavy use in the dark days.

The old captain smiled again as he remembered that morale had been very high with the officers, especially aboard the flagship. Commander Fitzjames had proved a very entertaining talker with many interesting stories. He would also amuse his fellow officers by imitating people. For example Ice Master Reid their old whaling captain with a very thick Scottish accent was a favourite of his:

'Ah. Now, Mister Jems, we'll be having the weather fine, sir. Fine. No ice at arl about it, sir, unless it be the bergs – arl the ice'll be gone, sir, only the bergs, which I like to see. Let it come to a blow, look out for a big 'un. Get under his lee, and hold onto him fast, sir, fast. If he drifts near the land, why he grounds afore you do.'

'Mr Jems, we shall soon see the Huskimays who live here. The whalers call them Yacks or Huskis for short.'

Soon after leaving Disko Island, the officers of Erebus had started a newspaper – *The Erebus and Terror Times*. This provided much amusement during the hours of darkness with only candles and lanterns to illuminate the ships. The newspaper was filled with articles by the various officers of their adventures in remote places. Sir John had contributed an account about small boat mapping on the coast of the American continent. They had all been amused by Fitzjames's piece about the desert heat, when he steamed down the River Euphrates in Mesopotamia. Goodsir contributed several articles about the creatures he had caught. He was also the subject of several cartoons showing him with his net over the side and various vast undersea monsters looking with interest at it.

Ice Master Reid and his crow's nest also provided some amusing cartoons. One anonymous cartoon had shown a log floating past the ship and Reid from the crow's nest calling down:

'It's the North Pole, sir.'

Franklin's thoughts went on to their first Christmas day together that had been nostalgic for most, as presents and packages given by loved ones for just this occasion were opened. He had opened a package containing a book and some warm socks and a note from his wife. The officers had also exchanged small presents amongst themselves, soap, cigars and books being most popular. Christmas dinner had been celebrated with good cheer and some very fine fare including the last of the fresh beef that had been saved for this occasion. They had toasted just about everyone they could think of, and finished with a fine sing song.

Next it had been time for New Year celebrations. Near the two ships, an area of flat ice had been used for sports, running, kicking around a ball and having sledge races. It was decided to celebrate New Year with a ball on this sheet of ice. The 'ballroom' was brushed clear of snow and roped off for the occasion. A rather poor ship's orchestra led by Lieutenant Graham Gore who played the flute, had been practicing for some time, yet the cold caused some of the instruments to malfunction.

Celebrations started aboard Erebus where the two crews assembled under the winter canvas awnings over the deck. It was crowded and lit by lanterns. First an extra ration of rum was issued and toasts drunk to the Queen, wives and sweethearts and many others. This was followed by a speech that the old captain had given to encourage the men and keep their spirits high.

The speech was followed by three rousing cheers for Sir John Franklin. The officers then led the crews out to the 'ballroom' and the 'orchestra' struck up. Some very amusing attempts at dancing on the slippery ice surface were witnessed. The officers had led off with some quadrilles that were followed by a hornpipe by the crew. At midnight the Royal Marines fired off a volley with their muskets and some signal rockets were also fired. The outdoor celebrations had ended then, as a bitter wind had sprung up. They had adjourned to their warm quarters aboard the ships with their heating systems operating full blast for the occasion. Each ship finished the celebration with a fine sing song.

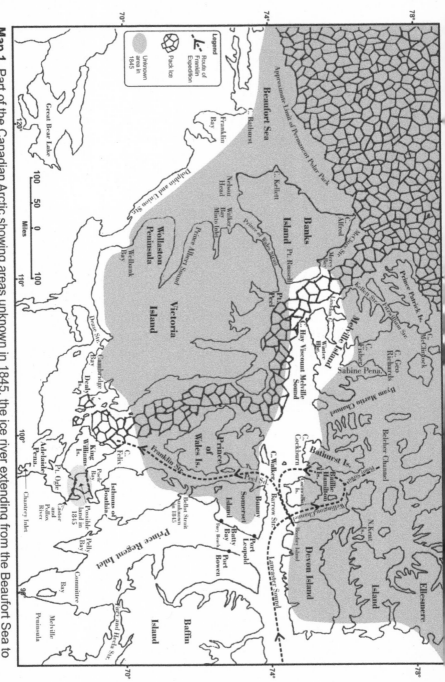

Map 1. Part of the Canadian Arctic showing areas unknown in 1845, the ice river extending from the Beaufort Sea to King William Island and the route of the 1845 expedition.

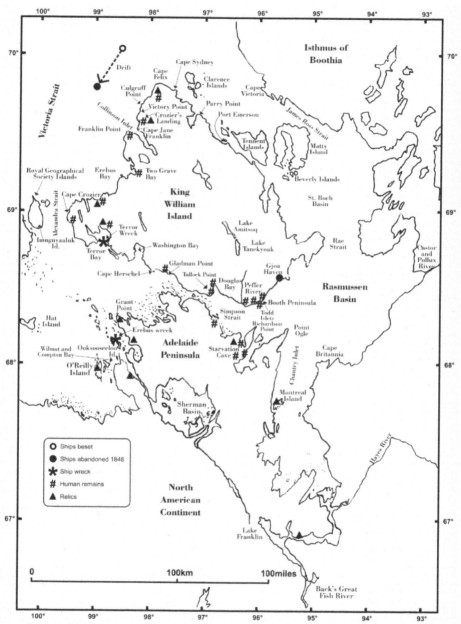

Map 2. The King William Island - Adelaide Peninsula area showing locations of remains of the Franklin retreats.

19

1845 CREW LISTS

These are the 129 men who went into the ice. When the expedition departed there were 134 men but 5 were repatriated from Stromness and Disko Island.

H.M.S.EREBUS

OFFICERS

Captain and Expedition Leader.... Sir John Franklin
Commander.. James Fitzjames
Lieutenants.. Graham Gore,
Henry Thomas Dundas Le Vesconte,

James Walter Fairholme
Mates.. Robert Orme Sargent,
Charles Frederick Des Voeux,

Edward Couch
Second Master...................................... Henry Collins
Surgeon... Stephen Samuel Stanley
Assistant Surgeon.............................. Harry D.S. Goodsir
Paymaster and Purser....................... Charles Hamilton Osmer
Ice-Master.. James Reid

WARRANT OFFICERS

Boatswain... Thomas Terry
Carpenter.. John Weekes

Engineer.. John Gregory

PETTY OFFICERS

Boatswain's Mate................................. Samuel Brown
Carpenter's Mate................................ Thomas Watson
Captain of the Forecastle.............. Philip Reddington
Quartermasters................................... Daniel Arthur,
William Bell,
John Downing
Sailmaker... John Murray
Caulker... James W. Brown
Blacksmith .... William Smith
Leading Stoker .... James Hart
Cook .... Richard Wall
Captain's Coxswain .... James Rigden
Captain of the Maintop .... John Sullivan
Captain of the Foretop .... Robert Sinclair
Captain of the Hold .... Joseph Andrews
Caulker's Mate .... Francis Dunn
Captain's Steward .... Edmund Hoar
Gun-room Steward .... Richard Aylmore
Paymaster and Purser's Clerk ..... William Fowler
Subordinate Officer's Steward ... John Bridgens
Stokers .... John Cowie,
Thomas Plater

ABLE SEAMEN

| Charles Best | Thomas McConvey |
| William Closson | John Morfin |

Charles Coombs
Robert Ferrier
Josephus Geater
John Hartnell
Thomas Hartnell
Robert Johns
Henry Lloyd
William Mark

William Orren
Francis Pocock
Abraham Seeley
John Stickland
Thomas Tadman
George Thompson
George Williams
Thomas Work

ROYAL MARINES

Sergeant .... David Bryant
Corporal .... Alexander Paterson
Privates .... William Braine,
Joseph Healey,
Robert Hopcraft,
William Pilkington,
William Reed

BOYS

George Chambers,   David Young

H.M.S. TERROR

OFFICERS

Captain .... Francis Rawdon Moira
Crozier
Lieutenants .... Edward Little,
George Henry Hodgson,
John Irving
Mates .... Frederick John Hornby,
Robert Thomas
Second Master .... Gillies Alexander
MacBean

Surgeon	John Smart Peddie
Assistant Surgeon	Alexander Macdonald
Clerk in Charge	Edwin James Howard Helpman
Ice-Master	Thomas Blanky

WARRANT OFFICERS

Boatswain	John Lane
Carpenter	Thomas Honey
Engineer	James Thompson

PETTY OFFICERS

Boatswain's Mate	Thomas Johnson
Carpenter's Mate	Alexander Wilson
Captain of the Forecastle	Reuben Male
Quartermasters	David Macdonald, John Kenley, William Rhodes,
Caulker	Thomas Darlington
Blacksmith	Samuel Honey
Leading Stoker	John Torrington
Cook	John Diggle
Captain's Coxswain	John Wilson
Captain of the Foretop	Harry Peglar
Captain of the Hold	William Goddard
Caulker's Mate	Cornelius Hickey
Captain's Steward	Thomas Jopson
Gun-room Steward	Thomas Armitage
Subordinate Officers' Stewards	William Gibson, Edward Genge
Stokers	Luke Smith, William Johnson

ABLE SEAMEN

John Bailey

John Bates

Alexander Berry

George J. Cann

Samuel Crispe

John Handford

William Jerry

Charles Johnson

George Kinnaird

Edwin Lawrence

David Leys

Magnus Manson

Henry Sait

William Shanks

David Sims

William Sinclair

William Strong

James Walker

William Wentzall

ROYAL MARINES

Sergeant .... Solomon Tozer

Corporal .... William Hedges

Privates .... James Daly,
John Hammond,
William Heather,
Henry Wilkes

BOYS

Thomas Evans,   Robert Golding

Note: Name spellings follow Cyriax (1939).

CHAPTER 1

*Expedition diary of December the first 1845 by
expedition leader Sir John Franklin*

M y name is Sir John Franklin and I was born in Spilsby in Lincolnshire on the sixteenth of April 1786. My father, Willingham Franklin, came of a long line of country gentlemen. He was a prosperous merchant who married a farmer's daughter – Hannah – and I was the ninth of their twelve children. One brother died in infancy and I am the youngest of the boys. We have seven sisters. My three surviving brothers, Thomas Adam, Willingham and John, and I found ourselves in turbulent and exciting times.

It was just after the French Revolution and Napoleon Bonaparte had assumed leadership of France that would lead to the Napoleonic Wars. Also the War of American Independence and its associated wars with France, Spain and the Dutch republic had just taken place. In England the Industrial Revolution was in full swing. The British Empire was expanding at this time. There were also many new and exciting new inventions, perhaps the most significant was the steam engine.

My brothers and I would meet in our hideaway in a large tree at the bottom of our garden and talk about these things. We had shared reading a copy of Daniel Defoe's 1719 book *The Adventures of Robinson Crusoe*. We would often play out parts. I well remember listening to my father telling us about the horrors of the Black Hole of Calcutta that happened in 1756. Perhaps it was not so surprising that two of my brothers Thomas and Willingham became interested in India. I was very close to my sisters, especially Isobella.

My brothers and I decided that life for us in Spilsby as merchants like our father would be too tame and so we resolved to leave the area where we had been brought up and seek adventure and our fortunes elsewhere in the world. As the youngest brother I was able to watch the progress made by my older brothers and sadly I have outlived them.

My oldest brother, Thomas Adam, raised a regiment of volunteer cavalry and led it. Unfortunately he made a disastrous financial speculation in which he lost his own and much of our father's money. He took his own life in 1824 at the age of thirty-three. My brother Willingham attended Oxford University, became a lawyer and went to India, where he was eventually knighted and became a Supreme Court Judge in Madras. Unfortunately he died of cholera in 1824 when he was forty-five years old. My brother James, who was three years older than me, also went to India, where he joined the Indian army and served in the Pindari War. He learned to speak Hindustanee and Persian. He was a surveyor, map maker and wrote a textbook on geology. He died at the age of fifty-one.

At the age of ten years I became a boarder for two years at Louth Grammar School, some fifteen miles north of Spilsby. There, I received a classical education, reading the Greek and Roman poets in their original languages together with playing sports. I did not find this training at all helpful in my later life. However when I was eleven years old, a friend and I walked ten miles from Louth to Saltfleet on the coast. It was the first time I had ever seen the sea, as my family had no interest in it. The vastness of the sea, the changing colours, the motion of the surface, the wooden ships with their towering sails and the harsh cries of the swooping sea birds, enchanted me. From that moment I was determined to go to sea.

The next holiday I went home and told my father of my decision. He was horrified. He wished me to join the clergy. However I was adamant and my father relented. He arranged a passage for me on a ship bound for Portugal. We had to cross the infamous Bay of Biscay with its ferocious storms. We did this and when I returned to Spilsby I was more resolved than ever to make a career on the sea. My father finally agreed. So when I was thirteen, my father obtained for me the position of first-class volunteer aboard the sixty-four gun man-of-war H.M.S. Polyphemus, under a Captain Lawford.

My life was influenced and shaped, not by what I had learned at Louth Grammar school but by two great men with who I served in the Royal Navy. One was my uncle by marriage, Captain Matthew Flinders, and the other was Admiral Lord Nelson. One of my aunts had married Captain Matthew Flinders and I was very keen to sail with him. Again my father helped. I joined my uncle aboard H.M.S. Investigator in July 1801 as a midshipman. This was my first but not last involvement with the 'Discovery Service' of the Admiralty. We sailed for Australia.

It was my uncle Matthew Flinders who taught me the skills I would need in later life. He taught me astronomy and navigation and how to make charts. My uncle took a personal interest in my education and cancelled my day watch duties, so that we could work together on navigation and map making. I was seventeen years old when we charted the Great Bight and Gulf of Carpentaria and made the first circumnavigation of Australia, proving it to be a continent.

My naval career was adventurous and I had the honour of fighting in several naval battles. Two of them, Copenhagen aboard H.M.S. Polyphemus, and Trafalgar aboard H.M.S. Belerophon were great victories led by Admiral Nelson. In addition there was an attack on New Orleans in 1814 in which I was slightly wounded. It was the battles led by Admiral Lord Nelson in particular that had a major effect on my life. Although great victories, the carnage and horror that I witnessed changed me forever. I was fifteen years old when aboard H.M.S, Polyphemus at the Battle of Copenhagen when Admiral Nelson destroyed the Dutch Fleet. I was nineteen years old at the Battle of Trafalgar aboard H.M.S. Bellerophon.

I will always remember the magnificent sight of the three fleets converging at Trafalgar and how our Admiral divided his fleet and broke the enemy line of battle for a great victory. It was a hard-fought battle and I was signal midshipman. When Captain John Cooke was killed, Lieutenant Price Cumby took charge of H.M.S. Bellerophon and used the ship courageously, engaging no less than five enemy ships – Aigle, Monorca, Bahama, Swiftsure and San Juan Nepomuceno. As a result he was made a captain at the age of twenty-eight. Bellerophon lost her main and mizzen masts and of forty-seven of us stationed on the quarterdeck, I was only one of seven not killed or wounded. Of our forty officers, thirty-three were killed or wounded.

To see so many of my friends and colleagues either killed or horribly maimed in battle and so much blood spilled had been almost too horrible to contemplate. I saw these actions not as glorious victorious battles but rather as unnecessary suffering and great wastage of human life. I saw the same thing at the Battle of New Orleans, when approximately 2000 Englishmen were shot down and their general Sir Edward Pakenham killed. Just as Admiral Lord Nelson had been at Trafalgar, both these great leaders' bodies were pickled in rum so they could be buried back at home with great honours.

I myself could never again stand the sight of blood, not even a flogging aboard a naval ship, because it would turn my stomach. This was a development I had not expected and to be a Royal Naval Officer who was essentially a man of pacific temperament did not bode well for my future. Happily there was a way out as shown to me by my uncle Captain Matthew Flinders on my second voyage. This was the 'Discovery Service' run by the Second Secretary of the Admiralty, Sir John Barrow. Thus I was able to quietly turn away from the warrior role and enter instead the role of peaceful exploration that was possible in the Royal Navy though the program of 'Discovery Ships.'

The Bellerophon battle story would have been much appreciated by my brothers and sisters in our garden hideaway in Spilsby. There were other adventures too. I was shipwrecked in Australia. At other times I was aboard ships to assist the Portuguese royal family escape the French army to South America, and to assist the Greek government. I made three polar expeditions. My first was in 1818 when I was second in command under Captain Buchan in an attempt to reach the North Pole via Spitzbergen. The second (1819 – 1822) and third (1825 – 1827) were overland expeditions to map the north coast of the American Continent. I was knighted for my overland Arctic work in 1827.

The main reason that I am here in command of this

expedition at the rather advanced age of fifty-nine years is because it provides an escape for me from what had become the darkest chapter of my life, as well as that of my dear wife Jane. I thank my Maker for giving me this opportunity to return to the clean icy wilderness of the north to do once more as I did as a young man in the company of other good men and stout ships of the Royal Navy. That is to explore and map unknown regions. Men and ships and sea and ice, I understand. It is my wish to regain some of the honours I once enjoyed following my early naval career.

All had been well, until I went with my dear wife Jane to take up the post of Lieutenant Governor of Van Diemen's Land in 1837. At first we were very happy with this splendid wooded and well-watered empty land. Jane in particular was delighted with it. She even climbed Mt. Wellington outside Hobart town – the first woman ever to do so. But there was no hiding from the harsh cruelty and depravity of that penal settlement with its 18,000 convicts held in separate prisons for men, women and children. They were heavily used as free labour by the settlers and most cruelly punished for even trivial infringements. Their only solace seemed to be rum and drunkenness.

Lady Jane and I did our best to improve their lot, and perhaps it was this that was seen as an attempt to unbalance a cruel system that greatly profited a few, which eventually led to my dismissal and recall. About a half way through our stay I discovered, to my great consternation, that John Montague, the Colonial Secretary of Van Diemen's Land no less – a man who was supposed to be my right hand and an ally – was working not only against myself, but also my dear wife Lady Jane. Worse still, he had visited England and had the ear of no less a person than Lord Stanley, the

Secretary for State for the Colonies, who had appointed me to my position there.

My reaction to discovering Montagu's attacks was to dismiss him, but he had the gall to take his tales to England and Lord Stanley, and my decision was overruled and Mr. Montagu reinstated, but at a new posting in South Africa. After that he flooded the newspapers of Van Diemen's Land and London with his accusations that as govenor, I relied too much on my wife's decisions. I could not protect my dear Lady Jane from his onslaught because she and I were equally attacked. I was accused of incompetence and she of writing my dispatches and generally playing a major role in the administration of the colony.

Whereas I have always been grateful for the helpful advice of my dear lady, who has been a wonderful companion with whom to travel through life's long journey, to have it distorted to such an extent, was most unpleasant. On my return to England I found myself unable to convince Lord Stanley of the truth, and I found him to be 'haughty and imperious.' So I found no alternative but to prepare a lengthy vindication and defence of my efforts and behaviour in Van Diemen's Land to be directed to Lord Stanley. Our departure has occurred before its publication, due in a few weeks, but I have arranged for a copy to be sent to Lord Stanley in my absence. Happily the expedition puts an end to these unpleasant worries.

The days leading up to the departure of our expedition from Greenhithe are memorable, not least because my dear wife Jane was at my side at all times. It was an exceptionally busy time. In addition to matters of the expedition and the ships, there were numerous social engagements. Jane and I attended numerous balls and receptions, which I found exhausting and finally contracted influenza that was most inconvenient. At the time Jane and I were lodging nearby to the ships. One evening I lay down quite exhausted on a couch with every bone in my body aching. I confess a moment of weakness and doubt and spoke to my Lady:

'Jane, my dear. I'm terribly tired tonight and I wonder if this whole expedition will prove too much for me.'

'Dear John, it's the influenza. In a few days you'll feel much better.'

'They should have chosen Commander Fitzjames instead. After all, he's only thirty-three years old.' My lady replied: 'John, please don't despair. Surely you can see that this is a great honour and opportunity for you? You must seize this opportunity and show the world what you can do in exploration, as you have done before.'

'Perhaps you're right and I shall certainly be pleased to be away from London.'

'John the the expedition will do you a lot of good for you have been fretting too much recently about your dispute with Lord Stanley and the Van Diemen's Land matters.'

'Yes, you're right, dear.'

'I don't wish to see you continuing to languish at home, and brooding over your Van Diemen's Land papers. If you remain here you'll make yourself ill. I'm sure the Admiralty gave you the command over Commander Fitzjames because you have far more experience than he has, as well as being very senior to him.'

What could I say? So I agreed with her and she put a blanket over me that I might sleep for a while.

Soon afterwards, for the last few days before sailing, Jane joined me aboard Erebus in the great cabin. I was proud to show her about the ships, that were now very smart with new yellow and black coats of paint. She enjoyed meeting the officers. The newspapers were full of articles on the expedition and we became the talk of London. Stories of my old adventures in the Arctic were once more revived. One evening we sat together in the great cabin of Erebus with a pile of magazines and newspapers on the table before us and we browsed through them. I commented:

'Well, my dear, you and I and our officers are indeed the talk of the town.'

'Yes, I hear that the crews are getting free drinks in all the taverns.'

I laughed and showed her one of the newspapers. 'Look, the *London Daily Chronicle* and the *London Telegraph* have described my former Arctic exploits and are citing me once more as "the man who ate his boots." I don't think that can be a compliment do you?'

'My dear John, I can think of a lot of entertaining remarks you could make to the ladies about the flavour and toughness of old boot. You're the only person in London with all its fine restaurants who has eaten boot you know,' and she laughed again.

'That disastrous land expedition of 1819-22 was well before we were married. Do you mind having a husband who once had to eat his boots?'

'Oh no my dear, not if it is the truth, for the sufferings of polar explorers are well known. That is probably why they've all been knighted, for it's a way for the government to expatiate its guilt over their sufferings.'

Jane then passed me a copy of the *Illustrated London News*:

'Look, dear, they're illustrating the ships. Here's a lithograph of the great cabin in which we're sitting. It even shows my portrait hanging up there. They also show Commander Fitzjames' cabin, and it looks very compact indeed.'

'It is nice to laugh together again, Jane, after all these long days of speaking of solemn matters.'

On Wednesday April the twenty-fourth, the ships were inspected by Sir George Cockburn, First Sea Lord, Vice-Admiral Sir William Hall Gage, a member of the Board of Admiralty, Lieutenant-General Sir Howard Douglas and Sir John Barrow, Executive Secretary of the Admiralty. This formidable team comprised the men responsible for the expedition, so I had the officers and crews well turned out and lined up on deck for inspection.

On the evening of Thursday May the eighth, Lord Haddington, First Lord of the Admiralty and the entire Board of the Admiralty gave a formal dinner at Somerset House in honour of myself, Captain Crozier and Commander Fitzjames and the officers of the expedition. In addition to the dignitaries of the Admiralty, also present were the presidents of the Royal Society, the Royal Geographical Society and the famous explorers of the 'Arctic Council.'

Everyone was resplendent in their full dress uniforms with decorations, swords and the traditional 'fore and aft' cocked hats. I felt very proud as I presented my expedition officers to their hosts in a long receiving line. But I thought some of my officers looked so serious that they must have found it formidable.

At dinner I was seated near Commander Fitzjames, my second-in-command on Erebus. This young officer came highly recommended with a splendid reputation and has been referred to as 'the handsomest officer in the Navy'. I found him both charming and entertaining. He was seated between the Second Sea Lord, Sir William Gage, and Sir Edward Parry. The former is normally a crusty and rather frosty man who never smiles, but he evidently found Fitzjames' sea stories highly entertaining, and chuckled a lot. For me it was the first time I had ever seen him smile.

Fitzjames' easy style evidently also entertained Arctic veteran Sir Edward Parry, who listened attentively to Fitzjames' plans to assault the North Pole on his return from the 1845 expedition. This seemed rather over-ambitious to me as Fitzjames as yet has no polar experience.

The next day there was a final inspection of the ships by Lord Haddington, Vice-Admiral Sir William Gage and Captain Hamilton. Many ladies and gentlemen of the public were also invited aboard the ships and were shown as much of the workings as we could get them to. The ladies' gowns are not at all suited to climbing around ships. But it was a very gay occasion with everyone in high spirits and there was much laughter. It gave some of the officers a chance to tell some very tall tales as well.

We had been due to sail on the fifteenth of May, but were delayed by the late arrival of much of the tinned food and some of the medical supplies. This had prevented the loading of the other food stores, because the holds had to be loaded in a manner, so that all items can be accessed as needed. I had looked with growing dismay at the stacks of tins of biscuits, hogsheads of flour, casks of barley and oatmeal, casks of salt meat, casks of sugar and peas, kegs of lemon juice and kegs of pickled cranberries, cabbage and onions that had accumulated on the dockside alongside the ships. Could there possibly be sufficient room for it all I wondered? Yet eventually it turned out that there was enough room.

Runners were dispatched daily all over London to complain about overdue deliveries and to hurry the deliveries up. The Victualling Yard at Deptford became frantic. Then the barrels of rum, and cases of chocolate and tea arrived to increase the store piles to mountains. Finally on the seventeenth, the tinned food did arrive and I was delighted to watch both crews struggling magnificently, without rest, to load the stores into the ships.

So at last our final day has arrived, as we depart Greenhithe tomorrow morning. Today it gave me great pleasure to read Divine Service for the first time for both ships companies mustered aboard Erebus. Present as visitors were my dear Lady Franklin, my niece Miss Sophy Cracroft, also my daughter Eleanor (by my first marriage). I took the ladies aside afterwards and addressed them:

'My dears, it's wonderful to see you three aboard this ship that will now be my home. I'll cherish this memory when we get to remote places. The ships and crews are both smartly turned out, and I want you to remember us like this. I will miss you all very much.'

The ladies murmured kind words along the lines of: 'But we will miss you too, John. Do please look after yourself and come home safely.'

'We may be away for some years and I am asking the three of you to be brave and not to fear for our safety. As you can see the Admiralty has provided the best in both ships and men. We are better equipped than any previous Arctic discovery expedition'

I then turned to my niece to say: 'Sophy, your mother Isobella and I were very close as children. I want you to know that it is a great comfort to me that you will be with my dear Jane as a companion during my absence. I am happy to know that Jane will not be alone while I am away.'

We then embraced each other and the ladies left the ship.

At ten and a half on the morning of Monday May the nineteenth, the ships left Greenhithe for Sheerness amidst great excitement. I was astonished to see that a crowd that I could well believe amounted to around 10,000 people crowded into the docks to wish us well and see us off. The crews, mustered on the decks, were looking extremely smart in new blue jackets and black handkerchiefs and the officers resplendent in their best uniforms. Bands were playing, speeches were made and there were rounds of cheering that rose to a loud roar as we slowly left the dockside. The navy's newest steam frigate, H.M.S. Rattler, took Erebus and Terror in tow. We were followed by our transport Barretto Junior, towed by the steamer H.M.S. Monkey.

I waved a coloured handkerchief as we drew away, hoping that my dear Jane could see me. We will proceed through the North Sea and each ship has taken a pilot aboard – William Hindhaugh and Peter Irvine - who will accompany us as far as the Orkneys.

As I watched the buildings receding, I experienced an immense sense of relief. The last few weeks had been made extra trying by the most unwelcome extra burden of the influenza. However I am delighted to be once again in charge of a major polar expedition. It is everything I could have wished for. Furthermore the break of the departure marked for me the final escape from what had become the darkest chapter of my life, as well as that of my dear wife Jane – being the problem of my dismissal as Lieutenant Governor of Van Diemen's Land.

But all that is now behind me and for the next few years we shall be out of contact with the civilised world and voyaging in the clean, empty Arctic wilderness. The admiralty has provided two specially-strengthened ships, H.M.S.

Erebus and H.M.S. Terror, that have been fitted out with new inventions including central heating of the lower deck of each ship, where the officers and crews will live. Each ship has a steam engine and a retractable propeller. We will be the first ships in the Arctic to be driven by propellers, although they must be used sparingly as we cannot carry great reserves of coal. The crews comprise selected experienced officers. Our warrant officers are also senior experienced men and all petty officers. The crew all comprises Able Seamen, and the Royal Marines. There are also four Boys First Class.

We will now pit our skills and specially strengthened ships against the arctic ice in the quest for knowledge and a North-West Passage. Such a sailing route would considerably benefit trade with the Far East. These matters alone will now become the very all of our existence.

CHAPTER 2

Expedition diary of September the thirtieth 1846
by Sir John Franklin.

There was great excitement aboard the ships at Beechey Island awaiting the summer thaw for our second year in the Arctic. We all hoped and prayed we would complete the North-West Passage this coming year. The very first glimpse of the sun's rim was made by Lieutenants Gore and Le Vesconte on February the third 1846. They had climbed to the highest point on Beechey Island in the hope of seeing it.

June became a miserable month for us because the sea ice in the harbour became covered in pools of meltwater and it was impossible to travel over it without getting a thorough wetting. But the skies are now blue and all over the land are splashes of colour as the spring flowers bloom. A big event for the ships was the return of each sledge party with its news and specimens.

Ice Master Reid, from his crow's nest with his telescope, had been watching Barrow Strait for several days and was able give us warning of an early breakup of the ice this year. At first he watched the colour of the ice change as the surface snow melted into pools of water to reveal the older bluish ice underneath. Then he detected small local movements that increased over several days, until on July the fourteenth the ice in Barrow Strait broke and great blocks could be seen rolling and grinding against each other with a tremendous roaring noise as they moved east down the strait. The officers and crews of both ships were soon up on the decks to watch this long-awaited striking natural event that is so important to us:

'There must be millions of tons of ice in motion over there,' said Lieutenant Gore. 'Some of the big blocks are being rolled over.'

I replied: 'Yes, but it is not yet time for our two wooden ships to be out there. When the ice has dispersed to the east, we'll get back into the strait'.

Turning to Commander Fitzjames, I gave him an order: 'James, it is now time to dismantle the magnetic observatories and bring them back on board. Can you please organise two sledge teams to go immediately to the observatories.'

Next I turned to Lieutenant Le Vesconte and gave a second order: 'I think we need to start the Erebus men cutting a channel through the ice of the harbour to the entrance to release the ships. It's about two miles. Please send a messenger to Terror and ask Captain Crozier to start another team on the same work.'

So there was suddenly much activity. The channel cutting had only progressed for three days, when suddenly a huge raft of ice in the harbour broke away from the land carrying the two ships with it. We moved slowly and majestically in our large ice raft out into Barrow Strait. Again north-westerly winds had cleared the north side of the strait of ice and our large raft soon broke up into many pieces. So on the eighteenth of July 1846, Erebus and Terror were once again free in the sea.

We worked the ships westwards along Barrow Strait past the southern shore of Cornwallis Island, watching closely for the south-leading channel that Ice Master Read had reported the previous year, also at a time of north-westerly winds. We were delighted when Reid called down that the channel to the south (today named Peel Sound) appeared to be open on its west side. I called my officers about me:

'Gentlemen, our orders are to proceed to Cape Walker, north of Prince of Wales Island and then turn south-west. However when we did this last year we found all the channels blocked by the ice river. Today we have a channel open to the south of us, but we've not yet reached Cape Walker. We have to decide now whether to turn south or whether to repeat the exercise we conducted last year by sailing further west past Cape Walker. Please give me your comments.'

Commander Fitzjames replied: 'Well, Sir John, it seems the Arctic does not open its doors very easily. We may have no other choice, seeing what we learned last year. Also the sailing season here is so very short at two months at best, that I do not think we have any time to waste looking for another open channel.'

The other officers agreed with these views, as I did myself.

'Very well then, let us turn south and try the channel. Please hoist the signal "Follow Me" so Terror will stay with us.'

With Terror following, we worked our way south across Barrow Strait, buffeted by the moving ice floes. The open sound lies between Somerset Island in the east and Prince of Wales Island in the west. The sound was much as it had been the previous summer with the north-westerly winds having pushed the ice across the sound to leave a narrow open water channel along the coast of Prince of Wales Island. We proceeded south along this channel with both our Ice Masters busy in their crow's nests all day long. But there were places where the channel became very narrow and we had to resort to the ice saws and ice anchors.

We worked our way slowly south for about 200 miles naming headlands, bays and islands on the way. Commander Fitzjames suggested we name the sound after Lady Jane, and so it became Lady Jane Sound on our charts. We arrived at the south end of Prince of Wales Island and saw again to the west the ice river again heading south. This proved to us that Prince of Wales was an island and that we had charted our second newly discovered channel in the Arctic. We continued to work our way south for another 100 miles when we arrived north of Cape Felix on King William Land. The area had been mapped by Sir James Clark Ross in 1830, when he sledged into the area from the paddle ship Victory in Prince Regent Inlet.

I opened the conversation with my lieutenants by saying:

'Everything we see to the south was mapped by Sir James Clark Ross in 1830, from the Victory Expedition led by his uncle Sir John Ross. Directly ahead of us is Cape Felix, the northernmost point on King William Land.'

Lieutenant Gore pointed to the west and said: 'All that hummocky ice over there must be the ice river described by Sir James Clark Ross. He reported that in summer when it breaks up, it's driven up onto the shore of King William Land.'

Next we turned to look to the east and I commented: 'There is only open water there and it must be the Poet's Bay of James Clark Ross, reputed to be open water every summer.'

'Yes,' said Lieutenant Gore, 'I was looking at the chart drawn by Ross and he shows Poet's Bay only by a dashed line. Maybe it's another Lancaster Bay like the one John Ross misidentified.'

So we put up a signal to summon senior officers to a meeting. Captain Crozier and Lieutenant Little came across in a whale boat to give their crew some practice. At the meeting James Clark Ross's chart was open on the table and we all studied it.

I opened the meeting: 'Gentlemen, we've arrived in our search area at last and we find ourselves blessed with open water. We must decide today on the best course of action.'

Commander Fitzjames responded: 'I've been reading James Clark Ross's account of Poet's Bay. It seems he has more than a strong suspicion that it's not a bay but might be a strait. I also know that Sir John Barrow believes it's a strait that probably links with Prince Regent Inlet. Bays shown on Arctic maps are infamous like the Lancaster Bay and Croker Mountains of Sir John Ross. May I suggest that as the only open water is in Poet's Bay, we should start our work there.'

There was some general discussion and I summarised it by saying:

'We're most interested in learning if the Poet's Bay of Sir James Clark Ross, seen only in misty weather, is in fact a bay or whether it links up with the summer open water channel along the north coast of the American continent mapped by Simpson, Dease and myself. Simpson and Dease carried their mapping in 1839 as far east as the Castor and Pollox River on Boothia.'

Captain Crozier spoke next saying: 'I'm particularly interested in Ross's description of a harbour suitable for wintering on the east side of King William Land in Poet's

Bay. He called it Port Emerson and it's in the Tennent Islands.'

The discussion went on for some time and centred on the great size of our two ships and their deep drafts. Erebus had drawn seventeen feet four inches when we left Greenland and Terror, being slightly smaller, had drawn sixteen feet. With the stores used on Beechey Island, both ships were now drawing about four inches less, but still with formidable drafts.

The meeting resulted in an ambitious plan for exploration of Poet's Bay. Erebus with her greater draft would proceed to Port Emmerson where she would form the expedition base. Two sledge parties would be sent out in opposite directions to map the eastern shore of King William Land. Meanwhile Terror would use her boats to make soundings ahead of her and work south towards the Matty Islands (named and visited by James Clark Ross), and if possible further south. Towards the end of the meeting I addressed Captain Crozier:

'Captain Crozier, I want you to take extra care with Terror and try to avoid any reefs. Make good use of your boats. Dease and Simpson managed to achieve record amounts of mapping using boats. See what you can do. Good Luck.'

I've decided to take the next part of this record from Captain Crozier's diary.

By the twelfth of August, Terror had passed the Clarence Islands and was approaching the Matty Islands in shallow water, where care had to be taken with many soundings from our two whale boats, working ahead of her. Around the Matty Islands we found extensive reefs, but from the mast head only open water could be seen to the south. This indicated that the dashed line boundary for the southern shore of Poet's Bay as shown on the

Ross map, was probably not correct. Nothing could be seen to suggest that King William Land might be connected to the Boothian Peninsula.

The distance from the Matty Islands to Castor and Pollox River is only eighty miles. As we were tied up for some time with sounding our way south, it seemed to me that we had an opportunity here to complete the mapping of what was increasingly looking like a summer open-water North-West Passage. I therefore ordered the two pinnaces to be lowered and manned, as these are our best sailing boats.

They were to be under the command of Lieutenants George Hodgson and John Irving. The boats were supplied for ten days only, but I urged them to return within a week. The winds were favourable and I directed them to proceed together, without stopping, the eighty miles to Castor and Pollox River, which might be completed in only two days. It would take longer for them to beat back to the Matty Islands, where they would find us working our way through the reefs.

So the two boats departed with high expectations on the fourteenth of August. We continued our slow progress of mapping the reefs in the approaches to the Matty Islands, in search of a deep water channel through them. It was while trying to find our way through the reefs, that an accident occurred to one of the two whale boats that were making the soundings. On August the sixteenth, a sudden squall caught one of the boats and drove her onto a reef, where she was stove and sank. Happily the crew, despite a good wetting, all got onto the reef and no lives were lost. They later reported that from the rocks they could see their boat inclined at a steep angle on rocks about ten feet under the crystal clear water.

The crew were picked up after the squall passed, by our second sounding boat, and brought back to the ship in a very wet and cold state, but happily without serious injuries. This probing the reefs around Matty Island is a very trying time, as we are so far from home with no shore base and the risks to the ship and boats are great. There seemed to be a narrow channel to the east of Matty Island and we worked Terror into this.

We spent another four days trying to find our way past the Matty Islands without success. We concluded that to continue south was no longer safe due to the shallow water and many reefs. I decide that it would be much safer to continue the mapping of the Matty Islands and the west coast of Boothia by sledge parties next spring. So I ordered that a cache of food be left on one of the Matty Islands.

At this time we had reached our furthest point south and were in the narrow channel between Matty Island and the Boothian shore. We sent two boatloads of stores to the nearest islet off the north-east coast of Matty Island. A cache was prepared with tinned food and sacks of flour, sugar, and oatmeal. The food was covered with sailcloth and large stones were placed on it to prevent the winds from blowing it away. The whole was then covered with a layer of sand.

We remained at anchor off the small islet, now with stores cached there, for another two days awaiting the return of the two pinnances. They were sighted on the twenty-third of August - the ninth day after their departure - working long tacks against the wind to reach us. I was greatly relieved to see them both returning. They came alongside at about four pm and the crews came aboard in very high spirits.

Lieutenant Hodgson immediately reported to me:

'Captain Crozier. Success. Success, sir. We sailed south continuously for a day and a half and reached the Castor and Pollax River at the latitude reported by Dease and Simpson. We have shown that Poet's Bay is not a bay at all. It is a strait that links with the summer open water channel along the northern margin of the American continent'

I was delighted for it meant we had found an alternative route for the North-West Passage. Further it is an open water North-West Passage route in summer. It also demonstrated that King William Land is an island and not connected to the Boothian Peninsula, as shown on current maps. This was excellent news indeed, perhaps tempered by the disappointment that we could not safely work Terror, with her near sixteen-foot draft, through the shoals around Matty Island. I called the crew together and addressed them:

'Men, our two boats led by Lieutenants Hodgson and Irving have had a great success. They've found a new open-water North-West Passage. Such news calls for a celebration. Let's splice the main brace.'

The announcement was greeted by three loud cheers from the crew. Smiles and happy chatter spread around and the returned crews had their hands shaken and backs slapped by laughing men. Sadly one older seaman came up to me and asked:

'Sir, does this mean we can start for home now?' To which I replied:

'I'm afraid not, as we are committed to mapping the area between Victory Point and Cape Herschel on the opposite side of King William Island before we can go home.'

While we were celebrating, Lieutenant Irving came to me and said that he thought we should name the newly discovered strait and North-West Passage route the "Sir John Franklin Strait". I agreed immediately, as we all thought that it would be a fitting tribute to the old gentleman, who would no doubt be delighted, even if it was only a small boat passage. It was a happy ship that piped down that night.

Next morning (August the twenty-fourth) we hauled up our

anchor and turned the ship northwards and started following our former route to rejoin Erebus. Unfortunately within two hours, a squall and snowstorm descended on us and we could not see our way, and in particular the floats we had left marking our channel. Before we could anchor, there as a violent jarring and Terror was hard aground on a ledge off the north-east coast of Matty Island. I immediately called out:

'Take in all sail. Make haste.' Men scramble up the rigging and began furling the sails.

'Leadsmen make sounding around the ship – both sides.' I soon had the information that we were hard aground forward with plenty of water under our stern.

'Launch the pinnaces. Attach a long cable to the spare anchor and we will try to kedge her off.' This was duly done and we laid the anchor astern of us. Despite the crew's best efforts at the capstan, we failed to move her. The wind then began to pick up and there was some working of the ship. After an hour we saw to our dismay several of the extra planks of the sheathing from the hull floating away, having been ripped off our bottom. The ship began to make water and the pumps had to be continually manned.

There was nothing for it but to lighten the ship. A pinnace was sent to Erebus to report our difficulties and request assistance. With several feet of water in the hold I was greatly concerned that the stores were not spoiled by seawater. So we loaded our last whale boat and a pinnace with stores from the orlop deck and the hold and transported them to a nearby islet. This islet lay off the north-east coast of Matty Island and after two days hard work, a tidy stack of stores stood on it. We had transported twenty-two large wooden containers filled with tinned food, flour and ships biscuits.

Two boatloads of men arrived from Erebus and they were a

great help in bailing to save the ship, setting up bucket chains to assist the pumps. Finally on the fourth day, with the kedge anchor in use, and four boats pulling Terror, we slipped slowly off the reef (August the twenty-eighth). But the ship was making water faster than the pumps could handle it. It was urgent to beach her before she sank. There was no possibility of spending some days taking the stores back aboard ship. We therefore made haste to sail to the west and into Port Emerson, where we beached the ship on a shingle shore on the evening of August the thirtieth not far from the anchored Erebus. Port Emerson had the extra advantage that if we failed to repair the ship before the winter freeze up began we were in a secure winter harbour.

There ends Captain Crozier's report on some very significant work. Aboard Erebus we had waited anxiously to learn what was happening. It was a great relief when Terror was sighted making for Port Emerson. Outwardly she looked fine but a little low in the water. But I soon learned it was only the bucket chains that were assisting the pumps that were keeping her afloat. Because of the water clarity Captain Crozier was able to bring her straight in and she gently grounded on a shingle shore.

Captain Crozier was soon aboard Erebus, making his report. I was delighted with his news of the open water North-West Passage that they had discovered and flattered that they had named it after me. It was also a significant discovery that King William Land was an island and not a peninsula of Boothia. There will be many new improvements to the Arctic charts as a result of our exploration so far. I spoke reassuringly to Captain Crozier who looked exhausted:

'Captain, I congratulate you on the success of your exploration. We have to take risks as the price we must pay for exploring in these northern latitudes in big ships. I also congratulate you for getting your ship off the reef and successfully bringing her here and beaching her.'

Captain Crozier replied: 'In order to lighten *Terror*, we left twenty two boxes of food stores on an islet off the northeast coast of the Matty Islands. We were unable to pick them up as Terror was leaking too badly when we got her off the reef. Can we go back for them as there are several months of food there?'

'I regret to say that we must abandon those stores,' I replied. 'To go back would put a ship at risk again of those reefs and also because we only have a few days left before the freeze up. If we can complete our mapping work next spring then we might be able to start home next year, in which case our provisions will be adequate.' Captain Crozier responded with:

'Sir John, I feel a great weight of responsibility for the loss of stores as we carried only enough for three years until July 1848, and those twenty-two boxes could have kept the men fed for some months. It will mean short rations. I therefore deeply regret this and feel responsible for having reduced our safety margin for survival. I also deeply regret the exploration time we have lost during the grounding and with more time still needed for repairs.' I continued:

'Let us now plan the work of repairing Terror as soon as possible for there is not much left of the summer.'

This was done. The *Terror* crew was moved ashore into a camp, while Terror was lightened and then hauled over, first to port and then to starboard, so that the carpenters and caulkers could repair her damaged bottom and recaulk the seams. The men of both crews worked in shifts through the days and nights and the repair work was completed in only five days of feverish activity. It would not have been possible for such a swift repair without the carpenters, men and equipment brought over from Erebus. We made great haste because we knew that winter would soon freeze everything and the exploration season would end within a week or two at the most.'

The day the repair work finished I called an officers' meeting in the great cabin of *Erebus*, which I addressed:

'The past two summers have been exceptional, with open channels that have considerably aided our exploration. I think we must make the most of this favourable weather and open leads to press on.'

'Sir John, we're in an excellent winter harbour here at Port Emerson, argued Captain Crozier. 'If we remain here we can complete the mapping next spring by sledge. James Clark Ross mapped this area from the Victory when she was in the ice of Prince Regent Inlet some 200 miles away. If we do this, we can return home next year in summer 1847 via the route we followed to get here.'

'Our orders are to sail through the North-West Passage if possible,' stated Commander Fitzjames. 'That means taking the route through the ice river on the west side of King William Land. I recommend that we take this risk since we're here. If summer 1848 will also be mild, then there's every chance that we could get through then. Besides it is the Navy way. We're here at great expense. We have had great success to get so far. Let us try to go the whole way. We have a very rare opportunity to be the first ships through the North-West Passage.'

Captain Crozier came back with: 'I cannot agree that to put both ships into the ice stream without a winter harbour is wise. If you must risk sailing though the North-West

Passage, then take Erebus and go. Leave Terror here in Port Emerson, so you will have an escape route to get out next summer. Lieutenant Gore can tell you what happened to Terror in 1836-37, when with Captain Sir George Back, the ship was trapped in a moving ice field and badly damaged. They barely got her back to Ireland, where she had to be beached.'

I had to say something here; 'Captain Crozier, the Admiralty orders specify that the two ships should stay together unless there is an emergency.'

This generated some discussion in which the two Ice Masters both supported Captain Crozier, and stated that it was unwise to enter the ice stream without a winter harbour. I decided to close the meeting:

'Gentlemen, this is evidently the most important decision we'll make on this expedition. I'd like more time to consider it. We'll close the meeting now and I'll go to my cabin to ponder the matter and to pray. I'll give you my answer tomorrow morning and we'll act upon it immediately, due to the shortness of the remaining sailing season. Thank you for your cooperation and I wish you all Good Night.'

CHAPTER 3

Expedition diary of October the thirtieth 1846
by Sir John Franklin

That night I hardly slept for the decision I had to make weighed heavily on me: to boldly enter the ice as Commander Fitzjames proposed, or to stay in Port Emmerson and complete the North-West Passage mapping by sledge parties next spring. Or even to take the third option, the compromise of Captain Crozier, of one ship left here and only the flagship to enter the ice. Clearly it is the key decision for the whole expedition.

So far we had had only success. We had found and sailed through two new sounds, proved Cornwallis and King William to be islands and have found an open water summer North-West Passage but suitable only for boats and small craft. Should we continue boldly with this good luck and try next to sail through what appears to be an ice-filled channel?

We had not yet completed the mapping required to show that a channel exists west of King William Island. We are here in the right place at the right time. Sir John Barrow has retired and it is therefore uncertain if the Admiralty polar program will continue. This is certainly my last expedition. Commander Fitzjames desires glory and I too would like go home a hero again able to forget the problems I underwent in Van Diemen's Land.

On the other hand Captain Crozier has the immense experience of five polar expeditions behind him and both Ice Masters also have lifetimes of experience in the ice. These three men urge caution and not to attempt the ice passage. But can I return home to England if I turn my back on the Arctic here and only send out a sledge party before returning home by the route that we came?

If we enter the ice it would mean working both ships possibly for as much as one hundred miles through the icefield, south into the summer open water. There is not enough summer left to complete it this year, but we would have all of summer 1847 to do this. All we need is one more mild summer.

I was up on the quarterdeck at four bells in the morning watch (six am). It was Saturday the eighth of August 1846 – a most memorable day. I wore my best uniform and sent a messenger below to Commander Fitzjames:

'Please ask Commander Fitzjames to join me and will he please put on his best uniform. Soon Fitzjames came scrambling up and saluted me:

'I see you have decided, sir.'

'Yes, I've decided to follow your advice, James, and take the bold approach – the "Navy Way" as you called it.'

'Wonderful, Sir John. If we succeed, think of the great honours we will gain, not to mention the £20,000 reward for being the first ships to sail through the Passage.'

'Let's get the anchor up and sails on as there is no time to waste. Flag signals for Terror to follow us if you please.'

Soon the order of 'All Hands On Deck' rang out and men began to scramble about following the orders of the officers and petty officers. I saw Captain Crozier come on deck and he looked startled, so I gave him a cheery wave.

As Erebus started to move, our crew began to cheer for they realised we were taking the bold approach to sail through the North-West Passage. We sailed along the north-east coast of King William Island towards Cape Felix - a distance of thirty-one miles.

Late on the eighth of September we rounded Cape Felix and began searching for a suitably long lead into the ice field. Around midday on the ninth with favourable winds from the north, we turned the ships south to start on our bold attempt to complete our orders by sailing through the North-West Passage. I could not resist a little drama at this crucial time. Commander Fitzjames and I wore our best uniforms and stood together on the quarterdeck. As Erebus heading south for the North American continent, entered the first open lead in the icefield, I had both our signal cannon fired. It was a gesture in this great empty wilderness that we the Royal Navy were here and our battle for the Passage was commenced. The crew loved it and gave me three cheers.

We are sailing to the west of King William Island, down what we hope is a strait (today Victoria Strait) with the objective of completing the mapping of the 100 mile gap between James Clark Ross's Victory Point of 1830 and Simpson and Dease's Cape Herschel of 1839. We hope with good fortune, another mild summer in 1847, our two experienced Ice Masters, and the assistance of the two steam engines driving the propellers, to work our way through to the summer open water channel, already mapped along the north coast of the American continent.

We are here at great expense with the best equipped expedition ever prepared for polar exploration. Because Sir John Barrow has now retired, such an opportunity may never arise again. We have in our hands the opportunity to make a bold approach and try to follow our orders to the letter.

To emerge in triumph after making the first voyage through the North-West Passage will be a great honour indeed. I do feel that both myself and Commander Fitzjames desire to achieve such honour and we have here a very rare opportunity to do so.

Indeed Commander Fitzjames is so keen to sail the North-West Passage that he has told me that before he left England, he wrote to his friend John Barrow Jr. telling him that when the ships emerge from Bering Strait, that we will make for Petro Paulowski in Kamchatka. He requested that his mail be forwarded there to be collected when we arrive. He also requested Barrow to arrange a fast overland passage across Russia for him to get to London, well ahead of the ships on their very long navigation back home. Should we get through the Passage then Commander Fitzjames intends to create a sensation in London by being the bearer of such good tidings.

So today we have started the hard task of working the ships along the leads in the ice. For this, we can use the steam engines and retractable propellers. It is good to see the steel-shod bows of the ships pushing aside and breaking up the thinner ice flows, that sometimes block the leads. But otherwise it will be necessary to use the ice saws to cut our way through the ice and then man haul the ship along on cables attached to ice anchors placed ahead of the ships.

We now have considerable experience of this type of work. Everything that could be thought of has been done to make the ships as fitting as possible for this work. Our ships were greatly strengthened both internally and with extra wooden sheathing, as well as iron plating forward to break up ice floes. We are the first ships in the Arctic ever to be propeller driven.

Our comfort is assured by the presence of central heating on the lower deck of each ship, where we live. It is a great pity that the John Franklin Strait proved too shallow to accommodate our vessels, or we might have been well on our way home already. We will not get through this ice field this season, for only a few days remain before the sea freezes over again. But we shall try our best and we have two very experienced Ice Masters to guide us.

I fear that Captain Crozier is in a black mood about my decision which he opposed along with the two Ice Masters. He even suggested we leave one of the ships at Port Emerson, so that if Erebus should fail to break though the icefield by summer 1847, when our supplies will be reduced to one year only, we could abandon Erebus and return home aboard Terror. Neither Commander Fitzjames nor I would consider this possibility, as it smacked of defeat and is not the Navy Way. In the Royal Navy, the loss of a ship requires a court martial.

We have no intention of returning home to a court martial. So aboard Erebus today there is a high state of excitement and glee, as we have made this boldest of decisions.

I cannot say however that the same happy atmosphere exists aboard Terror, where the Captain is known to oppose this approach and wears the most foreboding frown. He has not been seen to smile for a considerable time. We must now strive with might and main to get the ships through this ice field, as we shall then emerge with honour to travel home in triumph. The ships have stores that can be stretched to last until July 1848. That leaves us twenty-three months to escape the Arctic. If we can get another mild summer like the two we have just experienced, then I think our chances are good.

CHAPTER 4

*Expedition diary of Thursday the twenty-fourth of June
1847 by Captain Crozier*

This account of the expedition is here being taken over
by Captain Francis Crozier following the unfortunate
death of our leader Sir John Franklin on Friday the eleventh
of June 1847.

Perhaps I had better first introduce myself. My people
come from Ireland, where my ancestors of French origin
settled in the seventeenth century to avoid the English
Civil war. My parents George and Jane lived in Bambridge,
County Down and had thirteen children - seven girls and
six boys. I was the eleventh child. My father was a solicitor
and the town prospered with the industrial revolution that
brought a boom of linen making. At the age of thirteen years
I left home to join the Royal Navy during the Napoleonic
wars. My first ship was H.M.S. Hamadryad, a thirty-four
gun warship stationed at Cork. I participated in five polar
expeditions in the discovery ships of the Royal Navy

My last expedition was with Erebus and Terror to the
Antarctic. The expedition was led by Sir James Clark Ross
and lasted from 1839 to 1843. We twice wintered in Hobart
in Van Diemen's Land and were guests and friends of the
then Lieutenant Governor Sir John Franklin and Lady
Franklin. So Terror, which I captained in the Antarctic,
has been my home for much of the past seven years.

The sad day we lost our leader Sir John Franklin began when I received a message from Surgeon Stephen Stanley of Erebus to urgently attend the flagship. I arrived at Sir John's night cabin to find Surgeon Stanley and Commander Fitzjames with him. Sir John was lucid but very weak with shallow breathing. I took Stanley outside and asked him to report:

'Ah Captain I regret that I've the gravest of news. I've sat up all night with Sir John and have to report that he's fading. I don't think he will survive the day.'

"Are you certain he is fading? What ails him?'

'Although he is only sixty-one years old his body is worn out after his very adventurous life. His health has been in decline for some time. He has the body of man some ten or fifteen years older than his age in years.'

'But what exactly is wrong with him?'

'He has multiple complaints. I first noticed that Sir John's health was not good when we left England, but he went into a slow decline once we entered the ice. I think the enforced idleness in his role aboard ship had much to do with it, together was his habit of eating excessively and drinking at the table of the great store of wine and porter he'd brought aboard. He was stubborn and would not listen to my advice, but rather had decided to enjoy his time on earth. He had hoped to be home again for Christmas 1847 with his dear wife Lady Jane.'

'Yes, but you stopped his evening dinners with the officers when we were on Beechey Island.'

'He developed gout during the long winter on Beechey Island. At last he listened to me and I stopped him drinking wines and port wine in particular. As you probably noticed, he was able to move about his cabins and the wardroom in an increasingly slow manner. After we left Beechey, I detected an irregular heartbeat. It is now his heart that is failing him. His pulse is growing weaker and more irregular. He is lucid still and in the night we conversed about his approaching death. He has asked to see you this morning.'

'This will come as a terrible blow to the men. But I don't want them to know until it is over.'

Commander Fitzjames and I then sat with Sir John. He spoke to us rather slowly in a weak voice:

'Hello. Thank you for coming. I'm afraid Surgeon Stanley has some bad news.'

Commander Fitzjames who had become a very close friend of Sir John on the voyage spoke: 'Sir John, I'm devastated. Is there anything I can do for you?'

'James, when I'm gone I want you to help Captain Crozier as much as you can for he'll take over command of the expedition as stated in the Admiralty orders. I'd also like you to visit my family when you get home and tell my dearest Jane everything that happened and how successful we've been with our exploration for we've found two North-West Passages not one. I'm leaving a pile of letters for my ladies and for some friends and would be much obliged if you will see they are delivered.'

'But of course. Anything else?'

'My thoughts are for Lieutenant Graham Gore and Mate Charles des Voeux and their sledge team. They should return shortly to the ship with the news that their North-West Passage has been completed. Then God in his great mercy, will release you this summer, so you can all return home to report our successes and join with our loved ones for Christmas 1847. Goodby James.'

Commander Fitzjames shook hands with Sir John and left abruptly so we should not witness his tears.

Sir John then addressed me: 'Ah Francis, I'm very sorry to say but I think my time has come and I must hand over command of the expedition to you. I've prayed that the ships will be released this summer and that you will be able to lead the men and ships safely back to England. I've only one last request. After I'm gone, please see that I'm buried ashore and mark the grave so that my resting place will be known to our people back home. I'm sorry but I am very tired now and can talk no more. Goodby Francis. Goodby Stephen. Thank you for what you have done for me.'

About an hour later, Sir John quietly expired. Captain Fitzjames and I then assembled the men on each ship and broke the news to them.

On the morning of Saturday the twelfth June 1847, I held an all-officers' meeting in the great cabin of Erebus. I opened the meeting with regrets about the loss of our leader Sir John Franklin and summarised the highlights of his long career and his role in our present highly successful expedition. Next I confirmed my appontment as expedition leader by reading out Article 21 of the Admiralty standing orders for the expedition stating that I was to take command in the event of the death of the leader.

There followed a discussion of where and how Sir John's body would be buried. It was agreed that there would be a burial on land as he had requested. The site would be the nearest point on the shore of King William Land, some five leagues from the ships. Plans were made for a small campsite there where a gravesite in frozen ground will be prepared by two teams of men - one from each ship.

The death of Sir John has placed me in a most difficult

position. The decision to put both ships into the ice river was Sir John's alone and I together with the two Ice Masters had strongly advised against this move because of the lack of a winter harbour and the uncertainty of how long it would take to get the ships through. My suggestion that one ship only advance into the ice, was also overruled by Sir John. Sir John was influenced by the enthusiasm of Commander Fitzjames, who took a highly optimistic view that the ships would be through in one year – two at the most. That this route would be the correct way to return home via Bering Strait was laid down in the Admiralty Orders.

We expect the North-West Passage team to return shortly reporting the mapping of the last *circa* 100-mile long unknown stretch of the Passage. The ships are already in the channel in an attempt to sail through it. If we succeed, we can then sail the ships west along the known summer open-water channel along the northern coast of the American continent. This would be the first North-West Passage route ever and is one of the objectives of the expedition. I deeply regret our entering the ice river and unlike the optimism aboard Erebus, I fear greatly that the flagship has seriously underestimated the situation. Privately I even doubt my ability to extract the ships safely.

I therefore continued the meeting by giving a string of orders that surprised some of the younger officers of Erebus:

'Gentlemen, I would like work to start immediately on preparing both ships for their summer breakout along leads in the ice stream. These leads are expected to open in July. The canvas awnings encasing the ships are to be removed, the topmasts and topgallant masts raised and rerigged, also the yards and sails. At the same time parties are to remove the snow banks from around the ships that acted as winter insulation.'

My next comment surprised the assembled officers when I told them that I was not planning to immediately depart Terror and move aboard Erebus, as specified in the Admiralty orders. I said that Terror had been my home for most of the past seven years. I hoped the officers would indulge me if I did not immediately transfer from Terror to Erebus as specified in the Admiralty orders. Rather I preferred that Commander Fitzjames take over as Acting Captain for Erebus and Lieutenant Graham Gore become Acting Commander to take Fitzjames previous post.

This morning (Sunday the thirteenth of June 1847) two teams of men have gone ashore across the five leagues of ice to the nearest point on the north-western shore of King William Land. There they will prepare a fitting tomb for Sir John's final resting-place. It is a very desolate shore some eleven miles south of Cape Felix. The men are preparing a stone lined chamber about six feet deep in the ground that will be roofed over with slabs of rock now being collected from the ridges of rock debris that border the land. In order to mark the gravesite which would otherwise be inconspicuous on the flat desolate shore, a spare topgallant mast from Erebus has been sent ashore to mark the grave as a flagpole.

Yesterday (Saturday the nineteenth of June) Sir John Franklin was buried with full military honours on the shore of King William Land. It had been a logistical problem as the land is five leagues from the ships, so that overnight tents and a campsite had to be built there, first for the men tasked with digging the grave into the permafrost and second to provide accommodation for the officers and men who attended the funeral.

The men had made a special effort for Sir John and built a superb stone-lined grave four feet deep. The grave had been planned to be six feet deep, but the seamen worked for five days and broke four pickaxes just getting it to four feet, so it was decided that was sufficient. The roof was made of slabs of flat rock gathered from the beach ridges in the area. These were fitted together closely to prevent animals and meltwater from entering. Sir John was laid to rest in a magnificent mahogany coffin made by John Weekes our carpenter, from the finest red mahogany wood aboard the two ships. He wore his best uniform with his many medals and decorations.

Before the funeral party left the ships, I conducted a service on board Erebus for both crews and then all filed past the coffin to pay their last respects before the lid was screwed down. The coffin, draped in the union flag, was placed onto a sledge pulled by six of Erebus's seamen and taken ashore with a small burial party of selected officers and a guard of six marines led by Senior Marine Sergeant Solomon Tozer. It was a long days travel across the ice. In addition to myself, four officers from each ship attended along with three crewmen and three marines from each ship. Ashore I officiated and led a short service.

Fortunately the snow flurries that characterise this cold month held off for us. Marine Sergeant Solomon Tozer had his contingent of Royal Marines smart in their red uniforms drawn up on either side of the grave and volleys of muskets were fired in Sir John's honour. Happily there were no Eskimos around to witness this ceremony as they are as yet very unfamiliar with many of our customs. After the ceremony, I ordered that a part of the camp be left as a permanent hunting camp for future use. We already have another camp near Cape Felix some eight miles northwest of Sir Johns grave, which although a magnetic camp will also be used as a base for hunting.

Three days after the funeral (on Monday the twenty-first of June) the North-West Passage sledge party led by Lieutenant Graham Gore and Mate Charles Des Voeux and six men arrived back at the ships. Their return was greeted by high spirits as they had completed the mapping of the North-West Passage. A mood of euphoria swept the ships as the general feeling was 'Home for Christmas.'

This day (Wednesday the twenty-third of June 1847) I called a meeting of all officers in the great cabin of Erebus. The officers and crew of Erebus were in an ebullient and buoyant mood due to the success of the North-West Passage party. The talk was all about being home for Christmas 1847. However it was obvious to the officers that I was in a very serious and solemn frame of mind. It was a black mood with a barely controlled impatience, because I am finding it difficult to accept that my views on not putting both ships into the ice stream were overruled by Sir John.

Now that the ships are well into the ice, and as Sir John has died, the problem of extracting both ships, is now my responsibility. These days I can hardly bring myself to smile and am noticeably very formal and minimise my contact with Commander Fitzjames. I fear my measured tones and calm somber presentations had a similar effect to a bucket of cold water thrown over the happy gathering of Erebus officers.

I opened the meeting: 'Gentlemen, I consider this to be my first real meeting as expedition leader and will address a number of topics today. First I request Acting Commander Gore to make his report on the completion of the mapping of the North-West Passage, which was the main objective of the expedition'

This was done and then the matter of the problem of not finding Sir James Ross's six-foot-tall cairn and record at Victory Point emerged.

Gore reported: 'Despite a most careful search both on the way south and particularly again on the way back, no such cairn and record were found. Nor did it exist at the position given by the latitude and longitude estimated by Sir James Clark Ross. I'm confident that we located it on the way north and have left a record in a cylinder in a cairn that we built, at what we thought was Victory Point.'

'Commander Gore, I cannot agree,' said Crozier. 'Ross's cairn and record were not found, therefore the position of Ross's Victory Point is uncertain. The only fixed information available is the latitude and longitude estimated by Sir James Clark Ross. I therefore propose that in future Victory Point will be defined by these coordinates. The cairn built by Commander Gore might well prove to be a mistake.'

Poor Gore, who had been the toast of the Erebus wardroom the night before, was so crushed by this judgement that he was lost for words. Gore's 'triumph' had become Gore's 'mistake.'

I then continued slowly and deliberately: 'I wish now to share my views with you about the status of the two ships. Whereas it would be ideal for both ships to be released by the ice during the coming summer, to escape either north or south, this is very far from being certain. The rate of drift of the ships in the ice looks to be no more than one or two miles per year, and it might take several years to get through.

Therefore I wish to consider the situation with the two ships' stores. The ships were provisioned for three years, but the grounding of Terror in Poet's Bay resulted in the loss of a serious amount of these stores. This would be fine if the ships escape in the summer thaw of 1847. Before the loss of stores, at normal consumption they would last only until July 1848. In view of the uncertainty of the release date, I'm therefore ordering the ship-board food to be rationed at only two thirds the usual daily allowance. This means 'the four-upon-six allowance,' where four men's rations will be served to six men. Starting immediately the crews will eat 'short commons.'

Will Lieutenants Henry Le Vesconte and George Hodgeson work with Erebus Purser Charles Osmer, starting immediately to check the stores and draw up new lists for both ships in order to see if the stores can be made to last beyond summer 1848. Please bring your results to me as soon as possible. Because of the possibility of a food shortage if the ships are not released this summer, I want on all days of clear weather, hunting parties from both ships to be organised in order to supplement the food supply.'

By now the officers were silent and several looked shocked at the sudden change in the viewing of our situation that I had introduced. But I was far from being finished:

'Next I would like to consider the matter of fuel. Each ship was supplied with ninety tons of coal for use in heating and cooking and for working the steam engines. At the present time each ship has about thirty tons of coal left. This will be sufficient if the ships are released in summer 1847 and return home for Christmas 1847. However the supply is insufficient for a longer stay. I am therefore introducing immediately severe fuel restrictions. Winter heating of the ships will be reduced to only a few hours per day. Only one hot meal will be prepared daily.

Purser Charles Osmer, I want you to check the amount of fuel remaining on the ships and to make calculations for how long it will last making the above reductions and without using the steam engines. From now on, in times of fine weather, I want the hunting parties to follow the coast of King William Island in both directions to gather any driftwood to be brought back to the ships for additional fuel. I want the carpenters carefully to evaluate their wood stocks to see how much could be used for fuel, rather than for carpentry and ship repairs.'

But I had more to say:

'I'd like now to raise my most serious concern. Both ships are frozen into an ice stream where great masses of ice can move independently and we are without the usual protection of a winter harbour. I consider both ships to be in great peril from being crushed, rendered unseaworthy or even sunk, by huge moving rafts or blocks of ice, particularly during the summer thaw. Both ships have already experienced ice pressure, in particular the three days of pressure that delayed the departure of the North-West Passage party. You've all heard the specially strengthened timbers of the ships groaning and cracking at these times. At other times rumbling sounds have been heard aboard the ships due to distant motions in the ice field.

I remind you all that Terror was once badly damaged during winter of 1836-37, while trapped in sea ice when under the command of Captain Sir George Back. In summer 1837, with her hull frapped, the leaking ship had barely crossed the Atlantic to be beached at Lough Swilly on the Irish Coast. It was found that her keel including the rudder attachments had been broken and twisted under the port quarter. Commander Graham Gore was aboard her at that time if you want a first hand account.

Therefore the crews from today onwards will stand full watches and the lookouts be manned in daylight and in times of moonlight. I particularly want the officers to be alert to the danger and to ensure that the boats and boat crews are at all times ready for rapid launching. Oars, supplies and camping equipment are to be aboard the boats and other stores be boxed and placed on deck nearby, ready to be rapidly taken off the parent ship in time of danger from moving ice. I ask for extra vigilance on the part of the crew and the lookouts and to have all ropes, ice saws and ice anchors ready at a moments notice, should a lead open anywhere near the ships during the coming months of summer.'

What had started as a buoyant happy meeting ended in quite the opposite mood. I'd deliberately used the meeting to unburden himself of the worries I had long held and to share them with the other officers, especially the jolly crew of Erebus. All the officers are very aware that I've a vast record of polar experiences, having already participated in five previous polar expeditions before this one. My perspective is very different to that which had existed aboard the flagship up until the time of Sir John Franklin's death. The result was some very long and worried faces on the officers, as they digested the somber and dangerous picture painted by their new expedition leader.

Acting Captain Fitzjames tried to put some sunshine into the meeting:

'Captain Crozier, you paint a very bleak picture indeed for our prospects. It is the hope of all that the luck of the expedition will continue and that the coming summer might prove exceptional and provide an early release for the ships. It is my hope that the two ships will be able to work their way through the ice field to get to the summer open water channel known to exist along the northern margin of the American continent, so that the expedition might achieve its goal of being the first ships through the North-West Passage.'

There was then considerable subdued chatter amongst the officers in which comments were heard that all hoped Fitzjames would prove correct. However it is well known to all, that this is Acting Captain Fitzjames's first polar expedition. I then made my final address the meeting:

'Our scientific program should not be interrupted. The magnetic readings at Cape Felix camp will continue. I'd like a sledge party equipped for one-month duration to be sent out to follow James Ross's route to Matty Island and the supply depot which Terror left there a year ago. The party will replenish supplies and then proceed south to map the west coast of Boothia before the summer breakup of the ice. The party is to return to the ships by the route that they follow out, to take advantage of the two food depots on the Matty Islands. The party will take two sledges and consist of two teams each of two officers and six men, one from each ship. Thank you, gentlemen.'

CHAPTER 5

Expedition diary of the twenty-sixth of June 1847
by Captain Crozier

T his is Captain Crozier again, now continuing the
expedition diary started by Sir John Franklin. I now
come to the report made by the party from Erebus that
mapped the last unknown 100 mile section of the North-
West Passage lying to the west of King William Island. The
party was led by Lieutenant Graham Gore and Mate Charles
des Voeux with six seamen. The team was selected by Sir
John Franklin. While the team was away from the ship Sir
John died and was buried. The mapping team returned to
Erebus three days after the funeral. I have extracted this
account written by Lieutenant Gore from his diary

It was a very great honour for me to be selected by Sir John
Franklin to lead the all-Erebus North-West Passage team. Along
with mate Charles Des Voeux and six men, we were to set out
by sledge and map the last section of a North-West Passage.
But this one is ice-filled, unlike the passage found by Terror's
boats last year. Peter Dease and Thomas Simpson reached Cape
Herschel from the south in 1839, in a land abounding with
caribou and musk oxen. James Clark Ross reached Victory Point
from the north in 1830. The unknown section along the coast
between them is only around 100 miles.

It was planned that we should leave Erebus on Monday the
twenty-fourth of May 1847 and Commander Fitzjames had

already completed several naval message forms and had them sealed in metal cylinders for us to deposit at key locations along the way. We had everything ready on the twenty-third for an early departure on the twenty-fourth and had turned in for the night. At about ten pm, we were all awakened by loud rumbling noises and the ship trembled and shook. The night watch reported that the ice was moving along the port side of the ship. The movement was intermittent but lasted for three days. It reminded me of my days aboard Terror with Captain Sir George Back. There was much discussion, but the general feeling was that the ice stream was already beginning to break up early and that the hoped for release of both ships from it might occur later that summer.

However Sir John decided to delay our departure for a few days to be sure the ice movement had ceased for the present. This is because it is five leagues from the ships across the hummocky ice field to the northern tip of King William Island. We already have a magnetic camp ashore near Cape Felix where magnetic readings have been made since early this year. At present Lieutenant Fairholme and two men are living in the camp and we planned to visit them on our way south.

So we did not depart the ship until Friday the twenty-eighth of May. We took with us sledging rations for eight men for twenty-eight days. Before departure we had closely studied Sir James Clark Ross's description of his journey from Cape Felix to Culgruff Point, where he left most of his men and sledges, and proceeded south to Victory Point on foot accompanied by Second Mate Thomas Abernethy. The distance from Cape Felix to Victory Point is nineteen miles. At Victory Point they built a cairn six-feet high and left a message inside.

Although the track from the ships across the ice field had been marked and flagged by parties travelling to and from the magnetic camp, the recent ice movements caused some disruption and delay to us. But we arrived onshore on the evening of the second day and followed the markers to the magnetic camp. There we pitched camp alongside the magnetic team and ate our supper with them.

'Hello Fairholme,' said Gore 'Ti's a pleasant berth you've made for yourself. We come to join you but for one night only. We're out to map the last incomplete stretch of the Passage from Ross's Victory Point to Dease and Simpsons Cape Herschel.'

'Welcome Graham and Charles. We don't get enough visitors here. It's quite an honour for you both to be selected to complete the mapping of the Passage, also an all-Erebus team. Yes, our camp's comfortable. What news aboard the ships?'

'All's well, but our departure was delayed as the ice around the ships was moving for several days. No leads opened but there was quite a bit of displacement and the ships creaked and groaned. Sleeping was not possible some nights.'

'That's rather early for the ice to be moving, isn't it?'

'Yes indeed, but we regard it as a good omen indicating an early breakup of the sea ice,' I replied. 'You'll find the track back to the ships disrupted here and there, but we've marked out new sections on our way here.'

'Thank you Graham, It must have been an interesting experience.'

'Yes, the ice pressures reminded me of the time I was aboard Terror with Captain Sir George Back in winter 1836-37. The ice did terrible things to her and we arrived on the Irish coast in a sinking condition and had to beach her. I fervently hope that our ships will escape more ice pressures.'

'Come into the officer's tent and we will have some tea,' replied Fairholme. 'But I must ask you to keep your party and equipment well away from the magnetic hut, as it has to be clear of all metal objects.'

We entered the tent and sat down together. Fairholme asked: 'So if you complete this mapping of the unknown stretch of coast, we might be going home soon?'

'Yes we all hope for that. Commander Fitzjames is talking about our possibly being home for Christmas 1847,' I replied. 'But nothing is certain in the Arctic. Terror's Ice Master Thomas Blanky was trapped for four years in the ice with Sir John Ross before they managed to escape in boats to a whaling area.'

'Let's hope we have better luck.'

One of the seamen entered the tent bringing tea in to us. It was served in china cups with a blue willow pattern on them. This caused us some amusement. 'Good Lor' Fairholme, you've brought your comforts with you. T'is just like tea at home.'

'Well we must do what we can to make or lives comfortable.'

'We've brought two bottles of wine to share with you - one on the way out and the other on our return.'

The conversation wandered about and then Fairholme said:

'We're building a high pillar nearby on the orders of Sir John. It will be seen from the ships, so they can estimate the rate of drift of the ice. So far it does not look to be very much.'

We talked about the urgent need to complete the mapping of this last stretch of the strait (today's Victoria Strait) and that when it is completed the expedition's priority will be to get home. We then swopped amusing stories of small events and shared a bottle of wine

Next morning after breakfasting together, we departed the magnetic camp and set out south along the coast to locate Culgruff Point. This is not a straightforward task as the land is very flat and featureless and made up of ridges of shingle parallel to the coast. It is of a most dismal aspect, lacking vegetation and being still snow covered from the winter. We found it best to make progress along the coast by following a zone of smooth sea ice near the shore.

Culgruff Point turned out be a distinctive low point on an otherwise smooth coastline. It was here on his return from Victory Point that Ross had determined the latitude and longitude of the point. His coordinates for Victory Point were by estimate only. We marched on thinking a six-foot tall cairn would be distinct, despite the cover of about two feet of winter snow remaining on the ground. So we confidently followed the shoreline, keeping a careful lookout.

We were greatly disappointed not to be able to find the cairn. It just was not there. We confirmed this by arriving at the coordinated position given by Ross for Victory Point, that proved to lie well to the south of where the cairn was supposed to be. Confirmation was also given by our identification of Cape Jane Franklin.

'Well Charles,' I said, 'it's gone. There's no possibility that we've missed a six foot cairn as we've followed the coast most carefully. Presumably the Eskimos have taken it down. Perhaps there was a valuable tin or bottle inside with James Clark Ross's message.'

'So do we go back and look again for the stones that should be scattered about? But they might be buried under the snow cover.'

'No. Let's continue the main job of mapping the Passage as far as Cape Herschel. It's pretty clear that the strait continues. We can make a very careful search on our way north'

We had been instructed to leave one of the message cylinders at Victory Point, but could not do this until the point was identified. So we crossed the ice of Back Bay at the entrance to Collinson Inlet and arrived on the very distinct peninsula of Franklin Point. Here we built a cairn and left our first message *cylinder. We agreed not to waste any more time looking for Victory Point until we returned north on the way back to the ships.*

The coast continued to trend to the south-west where an ice-filled strait (todays Victoria Strait) separates King William Island from Victoria Island to the west. We arrived at a prominent headland that forms the westernmost point on King William Island, that we named Cape Fitzjames (today it is Cape Crozier). Rounding that, the coast trended ESE and the seaway became the narrow Simpson Strait separating King William Island from the Adelaide Peninsula, which is a part of the mainland of the American continent. We were thrilled to see the American continent and realised that we were the very first men to traverse the North-West Passage. We continued ESE along the coast crossing two bays. On the east side of the second bay we identified Cape Herschel and found the remains of the massive cairn built here in 1839 by Dease and Simpson:

'Well, Charles,' said Gore to Charles Des Voeux, 'it looks like the Eskimos have been here too and have largely torn down this cairn as well. Presumable any tin or bottle is valuable to them. I think we'll have to rebuild it before we put our message cylinder into it'.

'Fortunately Dease and Simpson made a big job of it and there is plenty of stone still remaining for a rebuild. But let's leave that until tomorrow and concentrate now with the men on getting a comfortable camp set up and a fine celebratory meal for the last link in our North-West Passage is finally completed.'

It was this section of coast that had been specified for completion on the Admiralty orders. We had traversed 100 miles of this flat stony coastline mainly by following the smooth ice near the shore. We had mapped the shoreline carefully and took time to obtain the best readings of latitude and longitude for the main geographic features. Two days later, we began our return trip to the ships. All was straightforward until we reached Cape Jane Franklin. Here we stopped rushing northward and took several days to carefully examine the next stretch of coastline to solve the mystery of the missing six-foot pillar at Victory Point.

We had sufficient supplies with us to take our time and do a thorough search and study. We took great care in this, our second search for Ross's Victory Point. Ross, in his uncle's book on the Victory expedition, did not provide a very detailed description of Victory Point. However, he did include a sketch map of the coast between Victory Point and Cape Jane Franklin. Fortunately we had brought a copy of his sketch with us. It proved very helpful to us now alerted to the fact that the six-foot pillar had been destroyed, presumably by Eskimos.

The sketch showed a shallow bay separating Victory Point from Cape Jane Franklin. After marching the coast several times, we concluded that the coordinated position of Victory Point lies in the middle of this bay, whereas Ross's Victory Point is the northern limit of the shallow bay. A careful search of Ross's Victory Point revealed a scatter of stones partially buried in snow that was probably all that was left of Ross's 1930 pillar. We rebuilt the pillar and left another message cylinder inside it. It lies a few miles north of the coordinated position. Satisfied that we had resolved the problem of Victory Point, we then headed north to spend another night with our friends at the magnetic camp near Cape Felix.

We continued rapidly along the coast and a few miles north of Culgruff Point, Mate Charles des Voeux suddenly pointed ahead:

'Look there Graham, I can see a flag fluttering. It wasn't there when we came south.'

'Yes I can see it too, I wonder what it means?'

We were so concerned that we hurried on ahead of the sledge party.

'Look, Graham, there is a camp alongside, but I cannot see anybody.'

When we got there we found the camp abandoned, although there was equipment inside the tents. The mast from which the flag was flying was a spare topmast from one of the ships. These things had most definately not been there when we marched south along his very coastline.

'Charles I can see a headboard and it looks like a grave. Somebody must have died aboard the ships.'

'Graham, it says it's the grave of Sir John Franklin and he died on June 11th. Oh dear what a disaster for the expedition and poor Lady Jane back at home awaiting our return.'

'How sad too that he did not live to know we have completed the mapping of the last link in the North-West Passage.'

We were both shocked and dismayed as was the sledge party when they caught up with us. Evidently our leader Sir John had died during our absence and had been buried here on this lonely deserted coast. We hurried on to the magnetic camp, where Lieutenant Fairholme and his men were delighted to see us again:

'Welcome back. Is the Passage completed?'

'Yes of course. But what has happened James? Was there an accident? How did Sir John die?'

'Apparently he died very quietly. Surgeon Stanley said he had been getting weaker for some time and his gout had hindered his movements. Surgeon Stanley and Commander Fitzjames were with him at the end. They said he was concerned that the ships would be released this summer and the expedition could go home once your party had completed mapping the Passage.'

'Did you attend the funeral?'

'Yes. It was quite a big affair considering how far we are from the ships. Sir John had requested to be buried ashore and that his grave be well marked. First a crew arrived to prepare a campsite. The location selected was the nearest point to the ships, because of the difficulties of crossing the ice field. Then the grave was dug into the frozen ground by two teams one from either ship taking shifts. It was made very nicely with stone walling lining it and large fitted stone slabs for the roof. Most of the stones were scattered about the area and had to be brought there by sledge. Then the officers and marines arrived after a one day march from the ships and camped the night. Erebus's carpenter John Weekes had made a fine headboard that you must have seen.

Next day the funeral took place. The service was read by Captain Crozier and a detachment of marines under Sergeant Solomon Tozer fired volleys with their muskets. The party stayed the night and then set out for the ships early next morning. Captain Crozier ordered the camp to be left standing as he wants parties out hunting and collecting firewood and it will be their base. Captain Crozier has of course taken over command of the expedition, and is I believe, making a lot of changes.'

'Firewood. Why do we need to collect that?'

'It seems that Captain Crozier is concerned about our fuel reserves.'

Our shared meal that evening was gloomy, as like the magnetic team we were all stunned by the terrible news. However the magnetic team listened avidly as we described the coastline we had mapped. Together we studied the now completed map of western King William Island. Next morning we set out in low spirits to return to the ships. We arrived aboard Erebus on Monday the twenty first of June. We had only been away for twenty five days but great were the changes *found aboard the ship. Commander Fitjames was now acting Captain of Erebus in place of Sir John.*

Our new captain and all aboard were delighted to see us and well pleased to know that the Passage, although ice filled, had been traversed and mapped. Fitzjames took up the cry of 'Home for Christmas' that delighted everyone. He told us that although Captain Crozier was now in command, he had delayed his transfer to Erebus from Terror as instructed in the Admiralty orders. He said that Captain Crozier had prepared a written order for me to take over the position of Acting Commander aboard Erebus to fill his former position. The next day there was to be an all officers meeting in the great cabin aboard Erebus chaired by Captain Crozier. I was to make my report there on the completion of mapping of the ice-filled North-West Passage.

The meeting today (Tuesday the twenty-second of June 1847) was something of a disaster for me because our new Commander in Chief, Captain Crozier was not in a happy mood. Fitzjames had tipped me off that this had been the case since Sir John died. Evidently Captain Crozier is not happy with our situation of being trapped in a moving ice field without a winter harbour. His suggestion to either winter both ships in Port Emerson or to leave one ship there, had been overruled by Sir John. Now that both ships are trapped in the ice stream and have already been subjected to ice pressure, Sir John had died. Captain Crozier had inherited a situation he would have dearly like to have avoided.

I made my presentation and Captain Crozier questioned me closely about the failure to find Ross's pillar:

'Commander Gore, are you certain you did not miss a six-foot tall pillar along the coast by cutting across a bay or travelling in a snow fall or fog?'

'Sir, we followed the coast closely both on the way out and again on the way back.'

'How certain are you that you finally found the correct position?'

'We found the sketch of the coast drawn by Sir James Clark Ross most helpful and believe his pillar was built a few miles to the north of the position given by his estimated coordinates. There were some scattered stones under a snow cover that might have been the remains of his pillar.'

'It appears to me, Commander, that the only real information we have are the estimated coordinates of Sir James Clark Ross. I don't want officers speculating on where the original pillar might have been. Henceforth I want Victory Point to be taken at the coordinated position and not where Lieutenant Gore thought it might have once been.'

There was a stunned silence around the table. I was too shocked to reply and I regretted that extra week of work we had put into the careful search for the missing pillar. It was especially disappointing for me after the very warm welcome and congratulations we had received on boarding Erebus. After that meeting my identification of Ross's Victory Point became something of a joke and became known as 'Gore's Mistake'. But there was no arguing with Captain Crozier in the mood he was in.

Here ends Lieutenant Gore's report. I have not omitted his comments about me because they are accurate. I am very aware that I am being hard on Gore and all of the officers of Erebus, but I feel there is an urgent need to impress on them the very seriousness of our position. Officers who can only see the bright side of the picture and refuse to think of possible problems and disasters and to plan ahead for them, are being irresponsible and shirking their duties.

To date the worries have been left to myself and the two Ice Masters. I want all the officers of both ships to be more aware of the possible grave dangers that exist here in the ice. They must be alert for signs of these and have plans in place to deal with any disasters. My role is to get them ready to deal with disasters as we are trapped in the ice river. It would really shock them to know how small I believe our chances are of escaping this ice river with the ships intact.

CHAPTER 6

Expedition diary of the fifteenth of July 1847
by Captain Crozier

During the morning of Wednesday the thirtieth of June 1847, there was a great commotion aboard both ships. The crews were busy rerigging the ships with the topmasts and yards already up and the sails being hauled up and being bent on. A cry from the lookout in the newly positioned crow's nest aboard Erebus, announced that a sledge party was sighted returning to the ships. Only four men could be seen pulling a loaded sledge and waving their arms in distress. Captain Fitzjames immediately sent out six men from the Erebus watch crew to assist in bringing the party in as soon possible. On both ships the doctors and medical teams stood by. Most of the crew came up on deck to see what was happening and there were many questions:

'What's happening?'

'Sledge party in sight giving emergency signals.'

'Where are the others?'

'Have they been attacked by polar bears or Eskimos?'

'What disaster can this be now?'

Ten days ago two sledging parties, one from either ship, and each consisting of six men and two officers under the overall command of Acting Commander Gore left the ships. They were to retrace Sir James Clark Ross's 1830 route back to the Matty Islands, where we left a food depot in 1846, as well as a large pile of our food stores taken out of Terror when she went aground. The Erebus team was led by Commander Gore and Mate Charles des Voeux, and the Terror team by Lieutenant Edward Little and Mate Frederick Hornby. The teams were to go to Matty Island and replenish their stores. They were then to cross over to the Ismuth of Boothia and map its west coast to the south. They were to carry supplies for four weeks, and then return by the way they went, so as to resupply on the way back. They had not been expected back for four weeks.

While we waited for the sledge to reach the ships, I checked with Terror's Surgeon John Peddie and Assistant Surgeon Alexander Macdonald that everything medical was ready. With the assistance of the watch men, the sledge approached rapidly and we saw one of the men (it proved to be Lieutenant Little) break off for Terror, no doubt to report to me. The terrible news reached both ships at about the same time. The entire sledge party from Erebus had fallen sick, but the Terror party were all well. Lieutenant Little had then, with three of his strongest men, pushed ahead for the ships with Commander Gore who was very ill, to get him back to the surgeons. Mate Frederick Hornby and the remaining two able bodied Terror men were assisting the less sick Erebus men back to the Erebus magnetic camp near Cape Felix.

Commander Gore was immediately lifted aboard and taken to his cabin, to be attended by Surgeon Stanley and Assistant Surgeon Goodsir. There Lieutenant Little and I joined them, bringing Peddie and Macdonald with us. A rapid examination of Commander Gore was made and it was evident and astonishing that this formerly healthy and robust man, who had left the ship in great enthusiasm only ten days ago, was now chronically ill. He appeared to be suffering from some form of strangulation, his vision was blurred and he could not recognise faces. Most disturbing was that his voice was distorted and speech was difficult. He had difficulty in swallowing the brandy that was offered. He was also physically weak.

Lieutenant Little reported:

'The symptoms began about a week ago but at different times to all men of the Erebus sledge party. First there were stomach cramps and diarrhoea followed by vomiting. I treated the men as best I could from the small medical chests carried. For the sick seamen there was a glass of brandy and for the officers, lime water to settle their stomachs, and asafoetida – a gum resin - used to stop stomach wretching. The men remained much the same but Commander Gore had rapidly declined.'

I called an emergency meeting in the great cabin of Erebus, where I spoke first:

'We've an emergency as an unknown illness has broken out.'

Assistant Surgeon Goodsir spoke next: 'It's strange that it has affected all of the Erebus party but not the Terror party.'

I spoke again: 'Lieutenant Little, you have done well to get the sick back to the Cape Felix magnetic camp and Commander Gore back to the ships. I would like a relief sledge party, including both of Terror's surgeons, got ready and to leave as soon as possible for the magnetic camp to assist the five sick men there. Meanwhile Surgeon Stanley what can you tell us about the illness?'

'We're not dealing with a light illness. Commander Gore is extremely ill and his survival is not assured. He is showing many symptoms, the worst of which is a form of strangulation. He has difficulty in breathing and his vocal cords are partially strangulated so that his voice is distorted. He has difficulty with vision. The treatment given by Lieutenant Little was correct and we are continuing it here but so far with no effect.'

Lieutenant Little then said:

'The illness at first was mild in all cases. Upset stomachs followed some hours later by vomiting. What was strange was that the two sledge parties were camped together and had each prepared their evening meals together but on separate stoves with slightly different combinations of tinned food. My party had eaten an assortment of tins, but Gore's party shared a single twelve-pound tin.'

Assistant Surgeon Goodsir interrupted:

'Could it be that the twelve-pound tin was poisoned?'

This led to some discussion of the symptoms and possible causes were considered. Lieutenant Little was asked to write down what he could remember of the two sledging crews meals on the evening when the illness broke out.

Assistant Surgeon Goodsir and I returned to the patient. The others continued with the planning of the relief party and the two Terror surgeons returned to their ship to make their own preparations for taking medicines and extra camping gear.

There was in fact little more that we could do but continue the treatment started by Lieutenant Little. So we tried to give more brandy with lime water and asafoetida. I asked Goodsir to sit with the sick man and went out to interview the healthy men of the returned party to establish in detail what the two sledge parties had eaten and how it had been cooked. It emerged that as the two sledge parties had not reached the Matty Islands, they had eaten only the rations taken from the ships. There was just time for me to take all observations across to Terror and have a meeting with surgeons Peddie and Macdonald before the Terror relief party departed.

Throughout the night Commander Gore's symptoms grew worse. Early next morning his breathing difficulties increased and his muscle activity weakened. Throughout that morning he experienced extreme difficulties with breathing, and by late morning he died of asphyxiation. We were all devastated and shocked, coming so close to the death of Sir John Franklin, it would seem that such a popular, strong character as Gore could not die. The ships flags were lowered to half mast and a great sense of sadness prevailed.

Another officers meeting was called in the great cabin of Erebus and Lieutenant Little was requested to attend. He reported:

'The two sledge parties travelled together and camped together but messed separately. Their fare was much the same, being the tinned meats and vegetables that were cooked over the spirit stoves. The cooking had been light because the main problem of the sledging parties is to make enough drinking water as the bottles of ether provided for cooking are rather minimal. Both sledge parties favoured the twelve pound tins of preserved food because the contents could easily be divided between the eight men of each team, to give a daily allowance of one and a half pounds per man. Nothing unusual had been noted by the sledging teams and the food appeared wholesome and good.'

Assistant Surgeon Goodsir reported: 'I asked the seamen who had accompanied Gore and des Voeux on the North-West Passage trip if they had noticed any unusual symptoms on that trip. It emerged that some of the party had also suffered from internal cramps and vomiting on their journey.'

I spoke next:

'We cannot eliminate the possibility that some of the tinned food is tainted. However the officers and crews have been eating the tinned food with relish for the past year and a half. Indeed we left behind a cairn built of the empty tins that had been consumed on Beechey Island. I would like to summon the two ships' cooks to the meeting.'

Erebus cook Richard Wall and Terror cook John Diggle are very experienced men both having accompanied Captain James Clark Ross and myself aboard Erebus and Terror in the Antarctic circumnavigation expedition from 1839 to1843. When they arrived I questioned them:

'Men, one of the sledging parties has become ill possibly from tainted tinned food. Yet we have not seen this problem before and the expedition ate this food on Beechey Island without any ill effects. Can you tell us anything about how you cook the food and do you check the opened tins before using the contents?'

The two cooks quietly spoke together for a while and then Richard Wall spoke to us:

'Sir, we're very aware of the possibility of tainted food. We therefore check everything before we cook it. It's long been our custom to give everything a thoroughly good boil on the coal-fired Fraser Patent stoves. Apart from a few blown tins, which we discard, we've had no problems with the tinned food.' Wall continued:

'However, we have noted that the camp cooking from the portable ether fuelled stoves is only light. In camp it is not possible to give the food the thorough good boil that we give it aboard ship. Perhaps this is the reason why the tinned food has served us well aboard ship but not so in the sledging parties.'

'Thank you. That's a most excellent observation.'

This led to some discussion about overcooking and undercooking and I summarised the results:

'I think the two very experienced ships' cooks have given us key information that is needed. It's been their custom for many years to give the tinned food a thoroughly good cooking on the coal-burning Fraser Patent stoves. In this manner there was no illness resulting from eating the tinned food during the first year. However the sledging parties do not carry enough fuel to thoroughly cook the tinned food. For this reason a tainted tin of food may be so undercooked that those who eat it can become seriously ill. Whatever it is, it's a very strong poison, judging what it did to Commander Gore.'

Commander Fitzjames then spoke:

'If the risk of illness is mainly with the sledging parties then we have a simple solution. Most sledging parties can be cancelled and the hands will concentrate on the preparations for the summer thaw and breakout of the ships. For essential sledging trips such as to the magnetic station, tinned food can be avoided and salt pork and biscuit substituted.'

I agreed wholeheartedly: 'An excellent suggestion, Captain Fitzjames, let us put that into force immediately'.

The meeting concluded that great care should be taken that wherever possible undercooking of the tinned food must be avoided.

The following day a petition of seamen approached Commander Fitzjames with the request that Commander Gore, who was an immensely popular officer, be buried at a special place ashore as Sir John had been. This was a popular suggestion with the officers of Erebus and Captain Fitzjames brought it to me.

Following some discussion, we decided that Commander Gore should be honoured by burial at Victory Point - the gateway to the last section of the North-West Passage that Gore and his sledge party had earlier completed exploring and mapped. This was agreed by Captain Fitzjames and myself, although I insisted that the site was to be that given by the coordinates of Sir James Clark Ross. A sledge party would be organised to go ahead and prepare a grave for Commander Gore that should be ready for use within as a short a time as possible.

The next day a sledge with two seamen arrived back at the ships with a note from Surgeon Peddie. It carried the worrying news that the five sick men were getting no better and several were in decline. He reported that he recommended to leave the men where they were at the magnetic camp, than subject them to the rigours of the sledge trip back to the ship. Assistant Surgeon Goodsir volunteered to join the two surgeons at the magnetic camp to assist with the sick men. I approved this, and Goodsir set out immediately with the same two seamen and sledge, also carrying extra salt pork and biscuits so that tinned food could be avoided.

Another party of men left the ship under the direction of Lieutenant George Hodgson to proceed ashore to locate Victory Point and prepare Commander Gore's grave. They were to mark a trail there across the seventeen miles of hummocky ice, as others would follow.

Hodgson later told me that they arrived at the site and found there a good supply of large rocks scattered along the coastal beach ridges. One of the crew who had been engaged in the digging and construction of Sir John Franklin's grave, suggested that instead of the very difficult digging into the permafrost and building an underground cyst grave, it might be quicker and easier to build a mausoleum-type grave above ground. This seemed an excellent idea and so they had proceeded to load selected large flat slabs of rock onto sledges and haul them to the site of the grave.

The site is near the shore, but up on a beach ridge of shingle now frozen hard with a snow cover still remaining from the winter. The snow cover was removed and a handsome grave was prepared measuring some six feet long, eighteen inches wide rising in a rectangular form for two feet above the ground level. A set of fine rock slabs was collected that could be fitted tightly together for a lid and the empty tomb was left for the funeral service.

Within two days two seamen had been sent back to the ships to inform that the grave was prepared and awaited the officers and the body of Commander Gore. This surprised us as no wooden coffin had been prepared yet. Commander Gore's body had been prepared in his best uniform and wearing his coat. So it was sewn into a canvas shroud as if prepared for burial at sea. When it came to lay his body in the tomb, one of the crew found and set up a rounded boulder as a 'pillow stone' for Commander Gore's head.

A fine wooden head board was carved by Erebus's carpenter with Gore's details. I led the burial service attended by Captain Fitzjames and selected Erebus crew. Afterwards the crew fitted together the stone slab cover and set up the headboard of the grave. We then spent an uncomfortable night crowded into two tents and next day we all returned to the ships.

On our return to the ships, I found it necessary to leave immediately for the Cape Felix camp for the burial of three men, including Mate Charles des Voeux. All had developed similar symptoms as Commander Gore had and died of the same suffocating illness. They were buried on a ridge behind the magnetic camp near Cape Felix. It was a black day indeed for everyone and we hope fervently that the ships will now be released this summer and we might return home for Christmas 1847. Our hopes were further lowered when two more of the four remaining men of the original Erebus sledge team also died, and were also buried on that ridge behind the camp. Only two seamen of the original Erebus party survived and returned to the ships eventually, both in weakened states.

CHAPTER 7

*Expedition diary written on the first of September 1847
by Captain Crozier*

As 1847 advanced towards summer there were signs of movement in the ice field around the ships. Yet the weather remained cold with much fog and snow fall. Aboard the ships, the effects of ice pressures had begun to be felt well before the death of Sir John Franklin. The pressures increased in power and frequency as the year progressed. The first indications of ice movement and pressure were in mid-March, when one night, a distant deep booming noise was heard that changed at times to a long drawn-out creaking groan, that sounded menacing. The sound stopped abruptly. The next pressure occurred on April the twentieth, following a gale in the middle of the month. The sounds of ice working to the east and west of the ships could be heard

The first ice pressure attack directly on Terror occurred on Sunday the second of May at about ten in the morning. The ship started to tremble and then we heard scraping grinding noises as the ship rose up and heeled to port. But the advancing floe broke and the ship fell back into the water. It was the first time she had been free since we became trapped. But there were no long leads to follow to escape. The pressure returned after a few hours, particularly at the starboard bow, where the flows broke and the pieces piled up against the ship. It lasted about fifteen minutes and then

Terror was driven forward and her bow rose up on top of the ice flow ahead. Loud cries of relief came from the crew as they realised that the ship was safe. The ice near the ship remained under pressure until around midday and then things settled down. Terror was left with her bows above the ice and with a five degree list to port.

The second ice attack on Terror occurred on the twenty-third of May and lasted for three days. This was the day before the North-West Passage party led by Lieutenant Gore, was due to leave, but the departure was postponed until the ice settled down. At about ten in the evening, the ship began to creak and groan. The night watch reported that the ice ahead and along the starboard side was moving. There was nothing to be done and the crew went to sleep. But loud snapping noises throughout the ship kept everyone awake. Officers with bunks on the starboard side could hear the ice scraping past the hull and battering it only inches from them. Few slept that night.

The noise stopped just before dawn, then began again in the afternoon and continued all night. The violent cracking of the ice, its groans and bumps made the ship jump and shake along her length. Many dressed and went up on deck. The pressure ceased on the following afternoon. But most of the crew were tired and nervous. The conversation at breakfast centred on how strongly built and reinforced the old ship was, but many were tired and on edge. We learned that Erebus had undergone a similar but lesser experience.

The North-West Passage party, did not depart until Friday the twenty- eighth of May, when we were sure that the ice pressure had died away. The crews were then allowed back on the ice for exercise and to practice sledge hauling ('pully hauly' of the men) including improvised sledge races. Some of the men witnessed a demonstration of the power of the ice, when a ten-foot thick raft of old blue ice was pushed against a neighbouring floe, so that both rose up into the air to form a pressure ridge. It was evident that such an attack against one of the ships would crush her easily. A sense of general uneasiness pervaded the ships.

The third attack began on the twenty second of June, when Terror began to tremble and a scraping grinding sound could be heard as the bow of Terror rose as a floe was driven beneath her. She was also shifted to port by the pressure of the ice. The worst pressure was on the stern, where floes began to pile up along the starboard quarter. This continued for twenty minutes and left Terror with bows raised and a ten degree list to port. All boats with stores in them were ordered lowered and moved onto the nearest large floe. The men were instructed to have their warmest clothing to hand, in case they too had to move onto the floe with the boats. But things remained quiet for the rest of the day and next day the boats were moved back on board. The following day I called an officers' meeting in the great cabin aboard Erebus and I did not mince my words:

'Gentlemen, as you are aware, the ships are experiencing great ice pressures. What is happening has been my greatest fear since both ships entered this ice field. We are on a lee shore, without a safe winter harbour. Last summer we had exceptionally warm weather and found the channels leading here open, as was Poet's Bay. However this year is proving much colder and we have not yet had a summer, but an extension of winter with much snowfall late in the year. A hoped-for summer thaw this year, on which we had staked everything in a bid to get through the ice stream to the open water channel along the northern margin of the American continent, now appears to be unlikely.

Instead of the open leads through the ice pack that we used last summer to get here, there are now few leads, but still there is motion in the ice field. The ice pressures to which the ships have been subjected are increasing in violence. Terror in particular seems more vulnerable, as she is not encased within a large floe as is Erebus. The whole ice field is moving slowly south at a rate of only about one or two miles per year. We are now in a most desperate state with the safety of the ships at risk and also with little hope of breaking out this year. I know the crews are ready with the boats, camping gear and stores on deck for rapid evacuation. I must urge you to be vigilant and get them off the ships if they look to be crushed.'

There was much conversation and surprisingly Commander Fitzjames managed to raise a laugh when he commented:

'The situation is enough to turn a man's hair grey.'

On Monday the twelfth of July the fourth attack began, when leads started to open in the ice river and Terror was released into the sea and floated in a small pool of sea water. Erebus remained locked into a large floe. At five pm the floes on either side of Terror began to close in. Many raced up onto deck to watch the events. Suddenly Terror heeled over twenty degrees to port. Everything moveable, ropes, chests, stores and men cascaded across the deck. Great clouds of steam filled the crews quarters as pots of water were upset into the fires of the cooking stove. Terror continued to heel over but stopped at thirty degrees.

From the deck it could be seen that a large floe had driven under the bulge of her starboard hull and was simply rolling her over. Everyone worked to restore order and our cook John Diggle managed to prepare a meal that was eaten by men sitting on the sloping deck with plates on their knees. At ten pm the floes beneath the ship drew apart and she slowly returned to upright. A round of grog was issued and the crews turned in at midnight.

The fifth ice pressure attack was the biggest one yet. It began at close to seven in the evening on Saturday the twenty-fourth of July. The lookouts reported seeing a wave of motion advancing across the ice field towards us like a sluggish shock wave. This was something I had greatly feared and had prepared the crew for it. I gave the order:

'All hands on deck. Bring warm clothing with you.'

Men poured up from below pulling on sweaters, oilskins and coats. As the pressure wave approached the ship, the entire surface of the ice became a colossal chaos of churning, tumbling destruction. The ice blocks jostled and banged against the sides of the ship until she was pinned against a gigantic ice floe and began to heel over onto her port side with the masts overhanging the large ice floe. Pressure ridges greater in height than anything seen before rose up between the floes. This astonishing amount of compression was caused by the ice field abutting against the shoreline of King William Island. Terror continued to tilt to port until she was inclined at twenty degrees, when the motion ceased. I gave my next order:

'Douse all fires and lights aboard the ship.' A great cloud of steam came out of the hatches showing that cook John Diggle had thrown water into the coal fired Fraser's Patent Stove. My next order soon followed.

'Launch the boats and haul them over to the large ice floe on the port side to be clear of the ship. Move the packed emergency stores and camping equipment from the deck onto the ice.'

'I want every man off the ship and onto the ice flow as soon as possible.'

By now the entire crew was working feverishly unloading the boats and equipment that had been placed ready for such an event. Captain Fitzjames sent over Lieutenant Fairholme:

'Good night Captain Crozier. Captain Fitzjames enquiries if Erebus can render any assistance?'

But I sent him back: 'Please inform Captain Fitzjames that we are managing. I would like him and his crew to stand by on Erebus for immediate evacuation in case she too is affected.'

The work continued all night. The crew managed to put up some tents to shelter from the cold wind and unpacked stores to assist the cook. Several men approached me:

'Beggin'yer pardon sir, but could we go back on board to collect some warm beddin' and more food for the cook?'

'No. I am sorry, but I cannot risk you being below deck. If the ship is tilted over any more, then many unsecured items will be falling inside the ship. You must wait here. If anything urgent is needed see Lieutenant Little and he will send you over to Erebus. But please remember that both ships are in grave danger until the pressure motions in the ice cease.'

By morning we had everyone assembled in a rather chaotic camp on the large ice flow clear of the overhanging masts of Terror. Our cook John Diggle had set up a rudimentary kitchen and had issued us with mugs of hot drinks and stew. We could see the crew of Erebus assembled on her decks, as they too stood by in the emergency. The crew gathered around me as we warmed our hands on our mugs:

'Well Capt'n what 'appens now?'

'All depends on whether the ice pressure has finished.'

But we were obviously out of luck, because around mid-morning the pressures and motions resumed. This time the ice was compressed, so that a number of ice floes rode up over their neighbours. Ice Master Thomas Blanky and Lieutenant Little came and stood with me. We watched in dismay as a number of these ice rafts moved over their neighbours until they abutted Terror's starboard side, tilting her some more. Thomas Blanky spoke:

'Captain it looks like a pressure ridge is formed along the starboard side of Terror. Look there is a third ice raft riding up over the other two.'

When this great block of ice reached the side of Terror, she was pushed over to about a forty degree list. I gave an order more to remind the men that we were still the Royal Navy:

'Stand fast men, but keep clear of the ship in case she is forced right over.' We watched the unequal struggle as the thousands of tons of ice pushed Terror out of their way.'

Suddenly Thomas Blanky shouted:

'Captain there's a fourth raft of ice riding up over the others now'.

Sure enough another raft rose up and pushed against the exposed bottom of Terror. It began to tilt her ever further over onto her port side. Loud cries came from the men:

'She's going. She's going. Oh no. Look out. No. No. No.' Some cursed and others called on their God. But Terror slowly rolled further over to port. Great rumbles and crashing noises came from inside her as loose objects fell to port.

Then with a great finality her masts and rigging suddenly crashed down onto the ice with a loud thump and splintering noises and the ice beneath our feet shook with the impact. Then there was a silence where only the groans and mutterings of dismay from some of the men could be heard.

I too was dismayed. It was a catastrophe. My poor ship that I had wanted to keep safe at Port Emerson, thrown over by the ice. Our home and means of transportation thrown over like a child's plaything by the unseeing, unforgiving ice. The men gathered around me. Some were weeping. That night of July the twenty fourth to the twenty fifth 1847 is one that none of us will ever forget.

To see my dear old Terror with whom I have shared so many adventures, my home for much of the past seven years, lying on her port side on her beam ends is a fearful thing. We had only just completed rerigging the ship in case we were released from the ice in the summer thaw. Now some of the top masts and many of the yards had broken and the rigging and sails were in a confused mess. Surprisingly there did not appear to be a great deal of damage to the hull, except for some planking to the upper hull, where the ice built up before she lifted and was thrown over. She is indeed a remarkably sturdy ship.

Happily, because the crew were ready and alert to my orders, no one was lost and there were only a few minor injuries, mainly by men slipping and falling on the ice, as they ran to escape her falling over. But inside, everything not secured had fallen to the port side. Our only consolation was that we could see that Erebus remained upright and safe from the pressures, as she was protected by being frozen within a large ice floe. However, neither ship had been released by the ice and it was finally clear that this year's summer thaw was not taking place. The weather had been more like winter than summer, cold with much cloud and snowfall. It looked as though we would have to remain here for another year, by which time our food stores would be near exhausted.

My first action after Terror went over, was to assemble all the men for a head count. Happily no one was missing. Next I addressed the men:

'Men, it seems our ship has been rendered uninhabitable. We must prepare a good camp for everyone right here on the ice. We may be here for some time. I will shortly take the officers to Erebus for an emergency meeting. Meanwhile I want to divide the rest of you into three work teams;

'Marine Sergeant Tozer, I want you and your marines to mark out and then build the camp here. I will shortly send the marines over from Erebus to assist you. Materials will be brought to you shortly. Drinking is not permitted'.'

'Petty Officers, I want you to divide yourselves and the crew into teams according to your responsibilities. One group will salvage canvas, wood and rigging to build tents for a camp and for storage. Please bring the materials to Sergeant Tozer. The other group will return to the ship, where everything that can fall inside has already fallen. They can start bringing out equipment, wood planking for tent floors, stores and kitchen utensils that will be needed in the camp. I urge this group to be careful as ice pressures may recur. If so, then get back onto the ice as fast as possible.

Now I must remind you that it is possible that the ice might one day release Terror. We may yet be able to reoccupy her. So I want you to conduct your salvage work with this in mind. The ship may yet take you home one day. So treat her with care. Good Luck and let us all camp together this night. I will now take the officers to an emergency meeting aboard Erebus.'

We made our way over to Erebus where Captain Fitzjames was most hospitable and all officers assembled in the great cabin:

'Gentlemen, we have a disaster on our hands. Instead of being released this summer, it looks as though we will remain trapped in the ice because it is an abnormally cold year. Terror is rendered uninhabitable, though perhaps only temporarily. As she lies at present, it looks as though her position is stable. She has been pushed up onto a large ice floe and is held there by a pressure ridge built against her bottom. It is composed of four ice floes stacked on top of each other. It may be a considerable time before the ice breaks up and releases her. Our greatest worry of course is that Erebus too might also be rendered unusable by the ice pressure. We must now make some new plans on how we will go forward.'

Commander Fitzjames spoke next:

'If we are not released, then both crews will winter aboard Erebus, as stated in the Admiralty orders.'

Lieutenant Fairholme then said:

'If both ships are destroyed or unable to escape the ice, then our most precious assets are the boats. We must take great care to preserve them.'

I replied: 'Yes, but they will not be safe left on the ice. In fact nothing is safe left on the ice, because it will be buried and frozen in with the winter snow.'

Lieutenant Le Vesconte came in with:

'Then we must set up a shore base. Indeed it should be a base able to supply us with everything we need to march out of here without the ships. That means it will be rather like the shore base we had on Beechey Island, except it will be five leagues from the ships.'

'These are excellent suggestions,' I said, 'but to move everything to a shore camp will be a major effort requiring both crews and there is not a great deal of summer daylight left in which to accomplish this. We must remove the stores, boats and camping gear from Terror. The camp on the ice which is being built right now must also be a temporary store for salvaged items from Terror.

Captain Fitzjames you may have to move some stores and equipment from Erebus, in order to make space aboard her for the accommodation of both crews over the depths of winter. I suggest the shore depot camp be built at Victory Point near Gore's Grave. There is already a track marked out showing the way to Victory Point, but it is likely locally disrupted by the ice movements.

There is a great deal to be done so let us divide the work. Captain Fitzjames I would like Erebus to provide sledging teams of six men each with two officers to start transferring equipment and stores to our shore camp. Terror's crew will be fully engaged in unloading Terror and salvaging equipment, spars and sails for re-use in the camps. For the present Terror's crew can camp on the ice alongside the ship. I suggest we name this temporary camp "Terror Camp". For the present I will remain on the ice with my crew.'

This was followed by considerable discussion which I had to interrupt:

'Today I want you all to concentrate on the problem of forming a land depot that will contain enough equipment, boats, sledges, and stores for the entire expedition to make a land retreat. Remember to protect the food stores from scavenging polar bears. The purpose is to be ready in case both ships are overwhelmed by the ice or fail to be released. We will have a separate meeting to discuss the amount of stores remaining and what course we will next follow.'

A month passed and considerable progress was made in unloading Terror and sledging the stores and boats to the shore depot of Victory Point. There quite a substantial camp had been built. On the twenty-fifth of August I called another officers' meeting in the great cabin of Erebus:

'Good day, gentlemen. I'm pleased to report that considerable progress has been made with transferring the stores and boats from Terror to the depot camp at Victory Point. Should both ships now be overwhelmed by ice pressures, then we have a base where we can assemble and the equipment there to make an overland retreat. Today we must face the options that remain open to the expedition. It is now sufficiently late in the year to see that there will be no breakup of the ice field this year and the ships will not be released.'

Lieutenants Le Vesconte then reported:

'Lieutenant Hodgeson, Purser Osmer and I have gone over the lists of remaining food stores. In short, the ships when they left England were stocked with food for three years. In particular we started with full rations for 137 men, but only 129 men sailed from Greenland. Therefore we carried full rations for 129 men for three years and ten weeks since the day we sailed from Greenhithe. So the stores at full ration should have lasted until August 1848. However we lost around five months of stores in the Matty Islands when Terror went aground. Our numbers have been reduced by seven deaths. So today we have stores to last 123 men on short commons for around fourteen months or until October 1848.'

I replied; 'Thank you, Lieutenant. That is a crucial date for it means we cannot spend the winter of 1848 - 49 here or we will starve. Summer 1847 has almost passed. Therefore I am forced to the decision that we must abandon the ships and march out of here in spring 1848.'

This was followed by considerable discussion that I allowed to continue for an hour, but little more was forthcoming:

'Gentlemen, thank you for your thoughts. I think we must go away now and plan out what preparations are necessary for us to assemble at the Victory Point depot camp and start a land retreat. There is much work in preparation to be carried out. We will probably take only four boats on sledges, as we cannot await the summer thaw of July 1848. The big question to decide is whether we retreat to the north or to the south, but there is plenty of time to consider that.

With a retreat now in view, I have decided that we must cancel the scientific program. Everyone will need to work for the survival of the expedition.'

'Captain Fitzjames would you please send out a two man sledge party to the magnetic camp at Cape Felix and bring everyone back please. I would also like to hear your thoughts on how Erebus will accomodate both crews through the worst part of winter please.'

'Yes, Captain Crozier,' Captain Fitzjames replied. 'I have given the matter some thought. It will mean extreme over-crowding, particularly for the three months of darkness. Whereas at present everyone lives on the lower deck only, the unheated orlop deck beneath might have to hold some men. Extra living space can be created aboard Erebus, by offloading stores and equipment. I thought for example to empty the rope store.'

The meeting ended with myself, Captain Fitzjames, Lieutenants Le Vesconte and Hodgeson and Purser Osmer going over the store lists once more to see if there was any way they could be stretched. Whichever way we looked at it, there were insufficient stores available for the expedition to winter over 1848-49. It left us with no option but to retreat overland at the latest in summer 1848. It would be unwise to wait for the 1848 summer thaw. The spring could be used to make distance on the retreat. So the boats would have to be man hauled on sledges, before the summer thaw in July. How greatly had our fortunes changed from the optimists who had thought we might be home again for Christmas 1847. At best it looks like we will all be crowded aboard Erebus for Christmas 1847.

CHAPTER 8

Expedition diary of Thursday the twenty ninth of July 1846 by Captain Crozier

The two days and a night when ice pressures forced Terror onto her beam ends were a time of extreme crisis for both ships and their crews. I had the latter well prepared and standing by for such an event and there were no deaths nor serious injuries. The entire crew of Terror moved onto the large ice floe on which the ship lay. As Erebus was also undergoing a crisis, it was left to the Terror crew to fend for themselves. In the crisis I turned to Marine Sergeant Solomon Tozer to assemble the marines from both ships to provide an independent work team to construct the camp for Terror's crew on the large ice floe on which she lay.

I then divided Terror's crew into three teams to salvage materials from the ship. This freed up the officers and I took them to Erebus to an emergency meeting. The Royal Marines from both ships worked together to lay out and build the ice camp or Terror Camp, as it is known now. I have therefore asked Marine Solomon Tozer who played an important role in the crisis to write an account of his day for the diary of the expedition. This follows.

I am a Somerset man, born in Axbridge, near Cheddar, in the north of the county. Before joining the Royal Marines in 1833 at the age of 18 years in Bath, I worked as a carpenter. I rose from private to corporal and was promoted to sergeant in

1844. It is unusual for a Royal Marine Sergeant to be making a log book of his own, but Captain Crozier has asked me to write an account of the events immediately after our ship Terror was thrown over onto her port beam ends by ice pressure. Captain Crozier assigned me and the marines of both ships to the task of building the camp on the ice floe alongside our overturned ship, thus freeing up Terror's crew to urgent salvage work. My old skills as a carpenter were much in use on this expedition, where I came to know Captain Crozier very well.

The building of the camp was a very makeshift affair, as we did not have enough tents for even a half of the crew. So shelters were made using eight foot pikes. However there was an abundance of materials on hand with the broken topmasts, yards, rigging and sails, now conveniently on or near the ice surface. The two Petty Officer Captains of the Maintop and Foretop Thomas Farr and Harry Peglar, along with blacksmith Samuel Honey led a team of seamen into the broken tangled rigging and starting removing spars, canvas and cordage that was delivered to us for camp building. Harry Peglar soon brought over several seamen dragging canvas sails:

"'ere y'are Solomon, there be plenty more where these come from.'

I ran over to Terror and called to Boatswain John Lane:

'John, can you supply us with wooden planks and a saw as we urgently need them to make floors for the tents. We cannot lie on the ice and snow. I will cut the planks to length as I used to be a carpenter. A coil or two of light line would help for the guy ropes and something to make stakes to bang into the ice to hold up the tents'.

'Yes I will send them over to you once we get inside the ship.'

He was accompanied by Boatswain's Mate Thomas Johnson and some seamen. They disappeared inside the ship taking with them Carpenter John Honey and Carpenter's Mate Alexander Wilson. They were after the carpenter's tools and his supply of wooden planks and timber. Another group entered the ship led by the three quartermasters together with the Captains of the Fo'castle and Hold, to bring out needed stores, camping and cooking utensils.

Surprisingly without the officers, the Petty Officers and seamen worked together well. The first tent put up was a sick bay for the lightly injured. Eight men had suffered minor injuries and a few small broken bones. There was considerable chatter about what the loss of Terror would mean to the expedition. The optimists of course, suggested that Terror might right herself in a few days and we all might yet escape with both ships.

It had fallen to me to arrange the layout of the camp and I followed the same groupings of the messes aboard Terror. One group of tents was for the officers, with a separate tent for Captain Crozier. I was not certain if, as expedition leader, he would not move aboard Erebus and take over Sir John Franklin's great cabin and night cabin. However we were not at all surprised to learn that he preferred to remain with his men, which we all appreciated. There was another tent for the mates, another for the Warrant Officers, and one for the marines. Three large tents sufficed for the crew. Then there would be extra tents in which to put more valuable salvaged stores.

It was not long before teams of seamen began to arrive with all the things required and the marines showed them where to put them. I showed some of the marines how to cut the floorboards for the different sized tents as they went up. By the end of the day, we had a new makeshift home on the ice which we called Terror Camp.

In the late afternoon Captain Crozier and our officers, along with Captain Fitzjames and many of the Erebus officers returned from their emergency meeting. The Captains and officers inspected the progress that had been made that day and seemed well pleased with the layout of Terror Camp. Captain Crozier came over to me:

'Sergeant Tozer I compliment you and the Royal Marines on doing a fine job on setting up our ice camp today. And thank you for putting me in a separate tent. I'm in no hurry to get everyone aboard Erebus yet. It will be necessary for the winter and will be overcrowded.'

Captain Crozier then called all the men together and addressed us.

'Men we have lost our home and also, it seems, the likelihood of sailing out of here this year. This I know is a great double blow to your hopes. However your training and discipline has resulted in no loss of life. We are all, at present, safe on this ice floe. You have worked well in the short time since the accident so that we have a comfortable camp – even with wooden floorboards in the tents.' This caused some laughter and cheers. He continued:

'There is great uncertainty about the future. We have just had an officer's emergency meeting. We have discussed the danger of losing both ships to ice pressures. Because it is still summer time, it is our decision that the best course of action is to set up a depot camp ashore on King William Island. In this way, if both ships are damaged and rendered unseaworthy, then the expedition will have a shore base from which we could march out of the area. It will mean taking some of the boats on sledges to the land depot.

I have selected the site of the shore camp to be at Victory Point where Commander Gore is buried. Captain Fitzjames is organising sledge teams to transport everything needed to the shore depot. The first two sledges with Erebus men will start *out tomorrow morning. Terror men will remain here to work on the ship and unload everything needed. As the camp and equipment depot at Victory Point builds up, some of Terror's crew will move and work there over the remainder of summer. When bad weather and winter darkness arrive in October, Terror crew will move aboard Erebus, in accordance with the Admiralty instructions. I would like Terror Camp to be moved ashore before the winter snow and darkness return in October. Some stores and equipment will also have to be taken from Erebus to the depot camp ashore to increase the winter living space aboard Erebus.'*

The report by Sergeant Solomon Tozer finishes here.

After three days on the ice floe, work settled down into a routine. The stores continue to be unloaded from Terror and are being placed in improvised tents. A cook shop and eating tent and a carpenter's workshop had been established on the ice. The Erebus and Terror carpenters worked to build sledges of different sizes. The smaller ones were to carry the camping gear and stores ashore and four large sledges were built to take four of the ship's boats ashore in case they are needed for an escape by land and water. The pinnaces were selected as they are the best sailing boats. Large amounts of canvas and rope have been gathered from both ships to make the land camp at Victory Point.

The first two sledge parties with lightly-loaded sledges set out for Victory Point, to mark the route. The marines were back in their capacity as armed guards. First to safeguard the piles of stores at Terror Camp from polar bears, and second to accompany each sledge party, again as protection against polar bears. The blacksmiths were busy making small copper cooking stoves, so that each tent party can cook their daily hot meal.

A month passed and today is Monday the thirtieth of August 1847. It has been a time of intense labour for both crews and the term 'pully-hauly' is now a much hated word, as it has occupied the men daily. Sledge parties are taking three days to cover the five leagues to shore, but only two days for the return to the ships with unloaded sledges.

A depot camp has been established behind Gore's Grave at Victory Point. It proved to be a very dismal place on very flat land made up of shingle ridges parallel to a low coast. Behind the camp, on a ridge of shingle about ten feet above sea ice level, a depot of stores was laid out over a length of the ridge of about 400 feet. The different items were stacked separately with wide spaces between. This was done so that the winds might keep the stores relatively snow free during the coming winter. From north to south were stacked: coils of rope; spare canvas; barrels of salt meat; barrels of flour and dried peas; iron; coal; spare clothing and uniforms and a stack of the smaller sledges.

Most stacks were covered over with canvas and loaded down with stones to keep them snow and ice free. The spare clothing was put inside a tent. Because of suspicions about the tinned food, none was moved ashore. The four boats on their sledges were turned over and placed alongside the camp. By early October with almost no daylight left, the last items from Terror Camp were moved ashore, so that Terror camp was finally abandoned. All men then moved aboard Erebus for the winter.

The officers were very pleased with the depot camp because it removed from them, the worry that should Erebus also be rendered unseaworthy by pressures in this great ice river in which we are trapped, the means will exist ashore for our survival and a breakout overland. I took over

Sir John Franklin's night cabin and put the Terror officers together in the great cabin. Whereas all crew had lived on the lower deck, now with two crews aboard, some men had to be moved down into the orlop deck beneath, where some of the store rooms had been emptied out for them. For these men it will prove to be a cold winter.

CHAPTER 9

Expedition diary for Monday the tenth of April 1848 by Captain Crozier

With both crews crammed aboard Erebus, we have experienced a winter (1847-1848) of what can only be described as pure hell and Erebus is today referred to as a 'hell ship'. Throughout the winter living in overcrowded conditions, we have been attacked repeatedly by the same mysterious illness that carried off Commander Gore and most of his party last year.

The attacks began aboard Erebus in August while the Terror crew were encamped on the ice and both crews were engaged in ferrying stores and equipment to the Depot Camp on King William Island. The total number of deaths to the expedition to date has been nine officers and fifteen men. Only the first three men and Sir John Franklin died of other causes. In the dark and extremely cold winter weather and situated some five leagues from the land, I ordered that the dead were to be placed in bunks aboard the abandoned Terror, still lying on her beam ends nearby. This we did for the sea was frozen to a depth of ten feet and the shore five leagues distant had the land frozen as hard as iron, under a thick blanket of winter snow cover.

For the four surgeons, in addition to attending the sick and dying, they also attended regular officers meetings in the great cabin of Erebus. There we tried to get to the bottom of the matter of the suffocating illness that was savaging us. At one of these meetings on Monday the twenty first of February 1848 we had a breakthrough. Surgeon Stanley was reporting:

'In addition to the fatal suffocating disease there have been some outbreaks of scurvy and several of the men including some of the officers are showing signs of a variety of problems, including mental affects. These take the form of lethargy, and even hallucinations. With the overcrowding, short rations and limited heating, Erebus has become a hell ship and we surgeons recommend as early a departure from the ships as possible. My own view is that the suffocating disease is aggravated by miasmas in the fetid atmosphere of the overcrowded ship.'

Surgeon Goodsir disagreed: 'I regret that I cannot agree with that view. I suggest that it is a poison contained in some of the tins of meat. I suggested this first for the death of Commander Gore, as his entire sledge party had become ill, whereas the second sledge party travelling and camping, but not messing with them, was unaffected. This winter's outbreaks aboard Erebus occurred when severe fuel rationing resulted in lighter cooking of food than in the past, due to reduced amounts of coal. The sledge teams living off salt pork and biscuit were unaffected.'

Surgeon Peddie spoke: 'We are agreed that all of the men who have died of the suffocating disease had eaten tinned food.'

At this point Assistant Surgeon Goodsir came up with new information that gave us a breakthrough:

'I must report that I found that there were around a half dozen men aboard who refused to eat the tinned food, as it is a new invention. I have made a study of these men and found that all of them are in relatively good health and that none contracted the suffocating illness.'

This observation proved crucial and much discussion followed. Surgeon Stanley then summarised the conclusions of the medical team:

'Captain Crozier, we realise that the expedition has been on short commons for a half year now. However we are today, in view of the new information presented by Assistant Surgeon Goodsir, forced to the conclusion that the only way we can certainly escape the ravages of the suffocating disease is to condemn the tinned food. This must result in even further reduction of the daily food allowance to dangerously low levels.'

Again there was much discussion but in the end I gave the order not to use the tinned food and to further reduce the daily food allowance. The result of this was that almost no deaths occurred during March and April 1848. Prior to this the death rate had almost reached one man per week and the funeral services conducted under the canvas-shrouded deck of Erebus were overly familiar. The burial detail would then take the body across to Terror, still lying on her beam ends, but linked with a rope line to Erebus.

At the next officers meeting the implications of the condemning of the tinned food were discussed. The main problem had become one of starvation and a crew that was rapidly weakening. There was no longer any question of waiting for the summer thaw of July 1848, as the expedition was now on a starvation diet. If we wait aboard Erebus to see if she is released, the food will be gone. If she is not released our fates would then be sealed. So we have concluded that the men will retreat overland.

There was much discussion as to whether we would

retreat north to Lancaster Sound and then into Baffin Bay, where we might meet whaling ships (a retreat route previously taken by Sir John Ross) or whether we should head south in an attempt to reach an outpost of the Hudson's Bay Company. Nightmarishly the nearest of the latter is on the Great Slave Lake some 1200 miles from Erebus. We had an officers meeting each month to consider the situation. For example in early April 1848, I opened the meeting as usual:

'Gentlemen, we're in need of a crucial decision and I would like to hear your views. By condemning the tinned food we appear to have stopped the ravages of the suffocating disease that has cost us so many lives. We're now on starvation rations and growing weaker. We'll attempt to march out of the ice river in which we're trapped. But we must decide whether to go to the north or to the south. Dr Stanley. could you inform us of the latest health situation please'.

'Yes, Captain Crozier. The crew have grown much weaker as the winter has progressed due to the short rations since the tinned food was condemned. We surgeons have thought of little else. It's our opinion that the crew's not sufficiently healthy to be able to undertake a long march. To march north would make us dependant on what stores remain at Fury Beach. These have now been on the beach for twenty three years and the antiscorbutics will have long ceased to be effective. We know from Ice Master Blanky of Terror (who had been with John Ross) that these stores were twice used by Sir John Ross on his 1829 to 1833 Victory expedition. Also we do not know if any remain there, as there was talk in England before we left that some whalers were planning to go there and bring them back to England to sell them. So we argue that the northern route looks unattractive.

However we do know that in summer to the south of us there is good hunting and fishing. Dease and Simpson built their cairn at Cape Herschel amidst great herds of caribou and musk oxen. Back reported a great abundance of fish in Chantry Inlet – the estuary of Back's Great Fish River. We therefore suggest a two part retreat to the south. We recommend that the crew be moved south to spend part of the summer hunting and rebuilding their strength with fresh food. A replacement diet of fresh meat and fish quite different to our shipboard fare is the only hope we see to restore the health of the men. When this is achieved the summer thaw should be here and the retreat can then continue by boat.'

I replied: 'A retreat to the south will need us to cover about 1200 miles from the ships to the Hudson's Bay outposts of the Great Slave Lake. This can only be achieved by using boats. The best route is probably up the Mackenzie River as Back reports many obstacles on the Fish River.'

Assistant Surgeon Harry Goodsir replied: 'If the men could get a few months on a diet of fresh food their health and strength should improve enough to undertake a boat journey along the shore of the American continent or a boat ascent up one of the rivers to the Great Slave Lake.'

Captain Fitzjames then said: 'It's my opinion that our greatest chances lie with the ships. However the present situation is impossible and I agree with what the surgeons are suggesting gives us an excellent chance of improving our health. Besides once the summer thaw arrives, we will have the freedom of the boats. It is not impossible that some might even sail back to Erebus, although it will mean returning to the same health problems we are experiencing now.'

Assistant Surgeon Macdonald spoke:

'The starvation diet is causing the men to weaken notice-ably each week. I urge that an escape from the ship and a retreat to the south should begin as early as possible.'

I then spoke again:

'Work has been progressing in preparations for the retreat over the winter. Wire-mesh snow goggles and stockings made from blankets have been prepared, along with sledges. Leather boots have been modified by driving brass screws though the soles so they can grip on the ice when hauling the boats. We have two boats ashore from each ship. The carpenters are already working on these boats at our Victory Point camp to lighten them as much as possible.

We have given a lot of thought to the amount of food we can take with us in the boats. A consideration of weight indicates that when we retreat we will be able to carry with us short rations for only forty days. The first objective of a southern retreat is to get to Cape Herschel on the south west coast of King William Island. A second objective will be Chantrey Inlet – the estuary of the Back's Great Fish River.

The distance from Erebus to Cape Herschel is 120 miles and to Chantry Inlet 210 miles. The mouth of Back's Great Fish River is about 250 miles from the ship. So the question is how many miles per day can we march, as we have to reach a good hunting or fishing area within that time. There we can hunt and recuperate until the summer thaw in July, when we will take to the boats. So in order to get to Cape Herschel in forty days we have to march three miles per day, for Chantrey Inlet over five miles per day and for the mouth of Backs Great Fish River over six miles per day. Commander Gore and the North-West Passage party reached Cape Herschel and returned in twenty five days, but spent some time searching for Ross's pillar at Victory Point. So his party averaged eight miles per day. In contrast James Clark Ross, who used dogs with one of his sledges, travelled an average of fifteen miles per day. We will be hauling heavy boats and have a weakened crew, so I do not expect more than six miles per day, which should put Chantrey Inlet within our range.'

So it was that our fate was decided.

A note added here at a later date: When the ships were abandoned the tinned food remained aboard them and little of it was taken on the retreat. We all hoped for a better diet from the summer hunting and fishing.

CHAPTER 10

*Captain Crozier's report of the 1848 retreat written on
Sunday the thirtieth of April 1848 in a tent in a snowstorm*

With the return of daylight in spring 1848, it was possible to relieve the crowding aboard ship by transferring mainly Terror men to the camp at Gore's Grave as it is now called. The two ships were abandoned on Saturday April the twenty second 1848. Everyone felt sad as we looked back at the ships. Erebus upright but still rigged for winter and Terror lying on her port side nearby. These ships had been our home for the past three years and we all regretted leaving them. Everyone was assembled at Depot Camp at Victory Point with the sledges loaded by the afternoon of Tuesday the twenty fifth of April. I sent Lieutenant Irving to recover the message cylinder left by Commander Gore at his Victory Point a year previously and additional messages were added to it. The cylinder was then left in a new cairn built near Gore's Grave.

The retreat set out on the morning of the twenty sixth of April, four boats on sledges and eight small sledges with camping equipment and food. But we were now only 105 men retreating, owing to the many deaths over the past winter – a considerable reduction from the 129 of us who sailed so confidently out of Disko Island, Greenland in 1845. We were now fifteen officers and ninety men only.

I marched at the head of the retreat in company with

Marine Sergeant Solomon Tozer. The two Erebus boats are the responsibility of Lieutenants Fairholme and Ice Master James Reid. The two Terror boats are under the command of Lieutenants Hodgson and Irving. The officers are each carrying a shotgun for hunting and a telescope.

We have taken the pinnaces as they are our best sailing boats. Our hopes for our lives lie with these boats. Considerable thought and effort went into preparing them for the retreat. Each is twenty eight feet long and has been specially lightened by the carpenters. The top five planks on either side have been replaced by light fir planks. Their keels, stem and stern posts have been planed down to lighten them and much of the iron work has been removed. Twelve iron stanchions have been placed along each gunnel and a nine inch high canvas spray dodger attached to keep out drifting snow. The oars have been cut down and each boat furnished with twenty four paddles, so that twenty four men can paddle each boat upriver when the time comes. In addition each boat carries fifty fathoms of line for hauling upriver. Each has a sail that can be used to assist the sledge and which doubles at night as a cover for the men who sleep aboard. With a similar sized boat George Back in 1835 succeeded in both descending and ascending the 530 mile long Great Fish River.

Most of the men sleep in tents carried on the sledges. The lightened pinnaces each weigh about 700 pounds and they are carried upon immensely strong sledges because of ice hummocks that have to be crossed. There was much debate before the sledges were built. It was eventually decided to make them extra strong because of the damage sustained to the sledges used to transport equipment and stores across the hummocky ice field from Terror to the shore depot at Gore's Grave last year.

Each sledge is constructed of two oak planks twenty-three feet four inches in length, eight inches in width, and with an average thickness of two and a half inches. These planks form the sides or runners of the sledge; they are connected by five cross bars of oak, each four feet long and four inches by three and a half inches thick, and bolted down to the runners; the underneath parts of the latter were shod with iron. Upon the cross bars, five saddles or supporting chocks for the boat were lashed, and the drag ropes by which the crew move the massive sledge, and its load, consisted of two and three quarters inch whale line. The sledge weighs around 650 pounds. So a shift of seven men hauling a sledge and boat weighing around 1400 pounds will have a load of about 290 pounds each to haul.

So on a grey unimpressive day with cold winds gusting from the north-west, and a leaden-grey sky, the 105 of us assembled into the four teams about the boats. Harnesses attached to the boats were picked up and put on. I did not think the occasion demanded speeches and spoke quietly:

'All right men let us begin our march.'

So all 105 of us set out together. Behind us we left much of the Depot Camp with stacks of extra equipment. We are carrying only enough supplies for forty days sledge work. It is generally known that it is I who favours the retreat to the south to what has been reported as rich hunting grounds. Captain Fitzjames is not enthusiastic about the retreat and favours remaining with Erebus in the hope of breaking her out and sailing her home. Perhaps as a result of this the retreat fell into the pattern of myself and the Terror party taking the lead and the Erebus party with Captain Fitzjames following.

Fresh food was our immediate requirement and so the officers were all ready to shoot any passing birds at this time of the year. The Royal Marines were divided between the four boats and carried their loaded muskets in the hope of killing for food. The hunting prospects are not good as it is still very early in the year, before the sea ice and winter snow begin to melt and there is no sign yet of the cold letting up for summer. Only one hour after departure snow began to fall and it became necessary for the hauling parties to close up so that no one became separated. At one point I marched alongside Captain Fitzjames, who was looking resplendent in his best uniform and officer's blue cloth overcoat for we have no special Arctic clothing, not expecting to retreat.

'Well James, we're in a ticklish situation. I appreciate your view that we might sail out of here on Erebus. But if we remain aboard ship until July when the leads in the ice open, then our food reserves would be too small to sail anywhere.'

'Yes, Francis. It's an alarming dilemma. If we march now we will have a chance in the hunting grounds to rebuild our strength. If we wait with the ships we run out of food.'

'The Dease and Simpson observation of abundant caribou and musk oxen at Cape Herschel gives us our best hope.'

'Well if the summer hunting proves successful, we will still have some choices of where to sail with the boats.'

'Yes. There will be a choice of whether to proceed to Back's Great Fish River or the Mackenzie River. The latter appears to be the easiest route from what I have read.'

'I'd also like to keep open the option of sailing back, that is if the men's strength is sufficiently recovered, with some volunteers to reman Erebus and try to work her south in this year's thaw.'

'A possible option that we can decide upon if the hunting is good and if the thaw looks better than last year.'

The retreat was following the smooth ice adjacent to the low flat shore of King William Island, where it was easiest to haul the sledges and avoided many of the ice hummocks further offshore.

'This is one of the bleakest places I've ever seen,' said James looking at the low flat shore of King William Island.'

I replied: 'The land seems to be made up only of gravel ridges.'

'That aspect reminds me of some stretches of the Euphrates River that I once steamed down in Mesopotamia. But there's no comparison between these lifeless wastes and the deserts of the Middle East which abound with camels, goats and gazelle.'

'True, but we have also seen some magnificent Arctic scenery when we were in Lancaster Sound in particular. Those snow-capped mountains with the sea below them filled with white and blue ice bergs was something special. Besides we know that in summer thousands of caribou will migrate into the area to feed on the summer flora.'

Our next concern was speculation on the distances the retreat might achieve each day. The retreat had left the ships early on the advice of the surgeons. The retreat has to get south to the reported rich hunting grounds of south King William Island and to the estuary of Back's Great Fish River as soon as possible in order to secure a supply of fresh food. As we can only carry forty days short rations with us, it is necessary for the retreat to cover at least five miles per day in order to reach the hunting grounds of the estuary some

210 miles to the south. It is good to have abandoned the condemned tinned food aboard the ships, but we are now in a perilous situation regarding a new supply of food.

That first day's march was not a great success because the snow flurries increased along with the wind strength and visibility became poor. In a lull between snow flurries in the afternoon we espied a small offshore islet that had partly been blown free of snow cover. An early halt to the march was called there and the four boats were drawn up opposite snow free land on which the tents were pitched. It was our first attempt at what was to become a very familiar routine. We had our first meal cooked on the small copper spirit stoves that had been built on board Erebus for the purpose. That first day we had achieved only two miles distance, but the retreat was finally underway and there was much hope in the hearts of the men.

CHAPTER 11

Expedition diary of the twelfth of June 1848
by Captain Crozier

The retreat has failed. We achieved only 100 miles in poor weather before a half of the men became too weak or sick to go on. A combination of unseasonably bad weather, heavy sledging loads and poor health of the undernourished crew has defeated us. It is a horrible realization that we are now trapped in a place so remote and with such a hostile climate that we were unable to march out.

The two Erebus boats had dropped steadily behind the two Terror boats. The two parts of the retreat had been out of contact for more than a week, when I halted the Terror boats on the shore of Terror Bay after thirty two days of travel including days lost due to gales and snowstorms. We stopped because the number of men unable to haul the sledges had risen to a half. Yet the distance we have covered from the ships is only 100 miles. We have averaged only three miles per day and yet the Hudson's Bay posts at the Great Slave Lake are still over 1100 miles away.

We put the two boats near each other and set up two large tents on the shore of Terror Bay. One for the weak or sick men and the other for the able bodied. We now await the arrival of the Erebus boats. I sat with my officers and we discussed our options.

'Lieutenant Little said: 'Sir, we're dismayed at the small

distances achieved, the weakness of the men and the impossibility of completing another 1100 miles.'

'Yes well we're unable to transport the half of the men who are too sick or weak to continue,' I replied. 'We can neither continue onwards nor go back as a single party.'

The discussion continued for some time and I summarised the results:

'It seems that the immobile sick must be left in the sick tent here in the charge of a volunteer officer and with at least one armed marine or hunter. The best hope for the able bodied is to return to Erebus and hope that she will be released in the summer thaw of July.'

Lieutenant John Irving spoke up: 'Captain I don't wish to return to the ships as we are hopelessly trapped there. I believe your original plan of move south into an area of good hunting is still sound for a small party. Summer hunting should provide food until the sea melts and then we can use the boat to sail along. I'd like to take any men who wish to continue with me. We'll have to start tomorrow morning because of the small amount of food left.'

'Permission granted, Lieutenant. Let me know later tonight how many men will be leaving with you.'

Next morning everyone who could came to say goodby to Lieutenant Irving and the seven men who had decided to accompany him. I spoke to Lieutenant Irving just before he left:

'John, when the Erebus boats get here there will probably be some who also wish to continue. If so I will send them after you. At worst they could catch you awaiting the thaw. So please mark your trail and keep a good lookout behind you for any of them coming along.'

There was still no sign of the Erebus boats, so we spent

a day in the Terror Bay area and shot a few birds. I was pleased to notice an abundance of stone rings marking Eskimo summer camp sites and other stone piles marking where they had cached their meat for the winter. I was sure we had entered an area of good hunting. Unfortunately it was so early in the year that only the birds were arriving. Terror Bay lies just on the south side of the big western promontory on the west side of King William Island. This was named Cape Fitzjames by the late Commander Gore (It is Cape Crozier today).

The day gave me a chance to consider what should be done next. We were now in a desperate situation with a half of the men immobile. I concluded that my role was to try to save as many lives as possible. Therefore the retreat should be abandoned and the strong men should return to the ship. We could leave hunters to look after the weak and sick men. The only hope for these men would be if the ship was released and we could sail her through the North-West Passage this coming summer. It was a long shot but the best option available.

That evening a very irate Captain Fitzjsames arrived with a small party of four seamen only. He marched up to me and shouted angrily:

'Captain Crozier, I've halted the Erebus boats in Erebus Bay some thirty miles north of here. A half of my men are unable go on. I cannot permit my men to continue what is now very obviously a death march. It appeared entirely pointless to me to abandon a half of them and to continue on in your footsteps with only the fit half of the crew and a single boat. I see our only real hope now is to return as many men as possible to Erebus and hope and pray that she will be released later this summer in the thaw.'

'Captain Fitzjames, look about you. Our situation here is identical. A half of my men lie in the sick tent. Lieutenant Irving left this morning with one boat and seven fit men. Our food supply is all but exhausted and the hunting has been very poor with only a few birds being shot. Obviously we cannot cover the 1100 miles to the Great Slave Lake. However I have pushed to this point and it appears quite different from the barren land we have covered. There are abundant signs of Eskimo encampments and food caches. I believe the area to be good for hunting and certainly better than the barren coast we have so far traversed.'

'So what is to be done with the sick men who are immobile and unable to return to the ships.'

'I don't think we have much choice. We will have to leave them where they are, but leave some able bodied men with them to look after them and hunt for food which should increase as the summer progresses.'

'If we can return to Erebus and restock her then if she breaks free in July we might be able to work her here and rescue some of the men.'

'That would be the only hope for any men left behind and they will have a chance with the summer hunting to recover.'

'Captain Crozier, the two Erebus boats are alongside small islets in Erebus bay about a half mile apart. A camp has been established on each islet adjacent to a boat. Two days ago I set off with one sledge and four seamen to catch up with you and the Terror boats. I left my remaining officers behind in charge of the two camps with the promise to be back as soon as possible within a few days. I called the men around me before I left and told them that I considered that the retreat had failed and it was my intention to lead a party back to Erebus, and that if any wished to continue south with Captain Crozier then they must march south with me. Only the four men with me volunteered. It took my small party two days of very hard marching to catch up with you, some thirty miles ahead of us.'

'I spoke with Lieutenant Irving about some Erebus men wanting to join him and he will be looking out for them. He left this morning and so is only a day ahead. He plans to stop further south and hunt while awaiting the thaw of the sea. Your four men should set out tomorrow morning to catch up with him.'

The next day the four men with a small sledge loaded with camping gear set off to the south to catch up with Lieutenant Irving. I then called the men together:

'The retreat is halted both here and in Erebus Bay because of the poor weather with many snow storms and because a half of the men are too weak or ill to continue pulling the heavy loads. We have achieved only 100 miles of our planned 1200 mile retreat, the message is clear. We are not going to get home by retreating overland. The immobile men will be left in three tents, one here and two in Erebus Bay. I want volunteer hunters to stay with them so that when the caribou and musk oxen arrive there will be abundant food. In the meantime birds and fishing will supply you.

The able bodied will return to Erebus, starting out this afternoon. If we can break her out in July we will work her south and may be able to pick up some of you.'

Volunteers stepped forward to remain with the sick as hunters. We would leave most of the remaining food we had with them and force march back to the ships carrying very little.

This we did taking two days to get back to the boats in Erebus Bay. There we repeated the process. Ice Master Reid volunteered to stay with the Erebus boat he had accompanied. He and Captain Fitzjames had a most affectionate parting.

The seventy miles back to Depot Camp at Victory Point became a nightmare journey for us and turned into something of a three day race for the strongest and a week long ordeal for the weakest. The men were spread out over twenty miles by the time the first got back to the camp. There Fitzjames and I organised the men as they came in. Finally I found that the failed retreat had reduced our numbers from the 105 men who left the ship to only fifty nine men who returned. Even with this smaller number the food problem was acute, as there was insufficient food to last out the winter, and much of this was the tinned food that had been condemned by the ships surgeons. But we had no other options than to eat it.

CHAPTER 12

Expedition diary of the tenth of October 1848
by Captain Crozier

The retreat had started out on the twenty sixth of April. We turned back on the thirtieth of May, arriving back at the shore camp of Gore's Grave on the fourth of June, with stragglers still coming in on eleventh. We placed ten of the men in a tent as a sick bay, as they had arrived back in poor condition. Only one of the two ships cooks – John Diggle of Terror - got back. Erebus cook Richard Wells was a much older man and regrettably he succumbed. Diggle soon had a kitchen operating. Hunters were out and a supply of birds was obtained. Otherwise we still had dried food, salt pork and salt beef in barrels in the camp.

My first concern on reaching the depot camp was to discover the status of the two ships. Left unattended, ice pressures might have further damaged them and with no one to attend any leaks, a ship could easily fill and sink. There was no holding Captain Fitzjames back and he left with ten of the fittest men almost immediately. They took two sledges carrying some food stores with them. Two of the men would be sent back to report to me the status of the ships. Provided that Erebus was intact, Captain Fitzjames would start the work of preparing the ship for a hoped for summer breakout. This was a big job as the ship had been left at winter quarters and the topmasts, yards and sails had to be rerigged. I would remain at the depot camp for a few days and start sending sledges of salvaged materials back to Erebus.

Two seamen returned only four days later with the heartening news that Erebus was in good order, just as we had left her, while Terror remained lying on her port side without change. This was a great relief to me for it meant we still had a home and a chance to break out of the ice in July when the summer thaw should arrive. It was also the signal to start sending men and salvaged stores and equipment back to Erebus.

There followed a very hard six weeks as the exhausted men salvaged as much of the stores, coal and wood for burning from both the depot camp and Terror as was possible in order to re-equip Erebus for a summer breakout. Perhaps we were fortunate, but the thaw came and the leads opened on the twenty second of July. We were not fully ready. One notable failure was to bring back to the ship the great store of surplus clothing that we had left in a tent ashore at Gore's Grave.

On the twenty-second of July, the ice was in motion and unlike the previous year, long leads began to open. We missed the cheerful presence of Ice Master James Reid who had volunteered to remain behind to look after one of the three camps of sick men in Terror and Erebus Bays. But now we had Terror Ice Master Thomas Blanky (a man who had already escaped with Sir John Ross after five summers in the Arctic) and he spent his days in the crow's nest.

On the twenty fourth of June (a memorable day for one year before on the same day, Terror was overwhelmed by ice pressure and thrown onto her port beam) a lead opened within 20 meters of the ship. It was a case of all hands out with the ices saws and then putting out an ice anchor and hauling the ship on the capstan. Very slowly Erebus moved into the channel and by midday was afloat for the first time since we were beset on the twelfth of September 1846. Some sails were put up in light north-west winds. Slowly we began to move south. We never stopped our efforts, having arranged the men into watches and working day and night to get the ship south. All realised that we had left about a half of the men sick and without rations for more than a week or two if they were halved. Their survival would depend on the hunter's ability and our being able to reach them as soon as possible.

Progress south was slow but steady, for the north-west winds persisted. On only three days we used the steam engine that gave us a few knots of speed. By the end of August, we had worked the ship to within sight of Erebus Bay and the big promontory of Cape Fitzjames on the south side of which lay Terror Bay. On August the twenty sixth I left the ship with a small sledge party to visit the three camps. I left Captain Fitzjames to continue working the ship to the south. We could see what appeared to be a channel (today named Alexandra Strait) lying between the western promontory of Cape Fitzjames and a group of islands lying to the south (today named the Royal Geographical Society Islands).

My sledge trip with just two men and one sledge is one of the most painful events of my life and is difficult to write about. Anticipating a difficult trip, I had elected to take only the two Assistant Surgeons (Harry Goodsir and Alexander Macdonald) with me. We reached the two boat places in Erebus Bay first. We had left them ninety days earlier. There was nobody left alive. All were dead.

Ice Master Reid was found in the stern of the pinnace that he had accompanied. He was lying in his sleeping position in the stern of the boat heavily wrapped in wolf skin blankets and canvas. On either side of him was a loaded shotgun leaning against the gunnel of the boat, as if in readiness to shoot any passing bird. Alongside him was a small pile of valuables, some of the silver cutlery of the officers that had been assigned to the crew and some of the officers pocket watches. In the bow of the boat were the remains of Erebus sail maker John Murray who was a particular friend of the Ice Master.

The adjacent shore camp was pure horror. One of the men at least had resorted to cannibalism and most of the men who had died were mutilated in his quest for food. It was the same for the second camp, but here the cannibal, now mummified, was still in the boat with his pile of mutilated bones and skulls, many of which lay alongside the boat where the bones had been split open for marrow. Having ascertained that there were no survivors, I immediately turned my small party away from the horrors and headed south. It had been very clear from the paucity of animal and bird bones that the hunting had failed dismally.

We marched south to the camp in Terror Bay, where we found the large hospital tent we had left there, although there were now a few graves outside. Inside the tent were many dead, and all mutilated by cannibalism. But horror of horrors we found that the last cannibal was still alive although very weak. It was a marine but we judged he was no longer sane. He had festooned his body with all the gold and silver valuables taken from his colleagues and had a watch on a long chain about his neck and a gold chain hanging from his ears. He was in such a low state that he could not get up and he did not recognise us but made some low groaning noises.

I spoke sharply to the two Assistant Surgeons:

'Doctors, outside the tent immediately if you please.' At some distance from the tent, I told them:

'It's too late to save the last man. We cannot take him back to the ship with us, as I particularly do not want the surviving men aboard Erebus to have any knowledge of the terrible end chosen by a few of the crew.'

The two doctors nodded their heads and I added:

'It's best we return to the ship and report that all have died of starvation because the hunting has failed. I feel it's my responsibility to keep everyone away from these terrible places.'

We then marched back along the coast towards Cape Fitzjames, where we were overjoyed to see Erebus with her sails up working her way through the channel between the Cape and the island group we had seen before (today called Alexandra Strait). We signalled the ship and a boat was sent to pick us up. I repeated my order to the two officers with me not to mention the cannibalism and that we would simply report that we had arrived too late and that there were no survivors.

Once aboard I informed Captain Fitzjames of the truth:

'James, it grieves me to report that we were too late. The men have died of starvation. There are almost no bones of hunted animals.'

Captain Fitzjames was shocked by my words and replied:

'Dreadful, dreadful news. But they were only left ninety days ago. What happened to the abundance of summer life, all the caribou and musk oxen reported by Dease and Simpson?'

'It must have been the lack of summer weather. There really has not been a good summer spell yet. It's proving an abnormally cold time. Perhaps the summer migration does not come as far north on cold years.'

'I'm very sorry to hear that. It's as well we returned to the ships or we might all have perished too because of poor hunting'.

'There's worse to come yet James. At both tents in Erebus Bay and at the tent in Terror Bay, the dead had been mutilated by cannibalism. It may only have been one man or two at the most at each place, but they evidently lived a long time off the dead. They were identifiable because their bodies were still intact. Worse yet was that the cannibal at the hospital tent at Terror Bay still had some life in him yet. He was far gone and made only groaning noises and did not recognise us. He had covered himself in all the valuable jewellery he could find. We left him there. Under no circumstances do I want this information to reach the crew. It would destroy what is left of their morale.'

'I could not agree more Francis. Who would think that British seamen could resort to cannibalism?'

We talked some more and James asked me:

'Tell me did you see anything of my friend Ice Master James Reid?' So I described what I had seen and James hung his head in silence.

It was now the end of the first week of September and the sea was beginning to freeze again. We had almost worked our way south between the islands and could see the tent in Terror Bay in the distance. However I kept the ship turned away from Terror Bay and eventually I directed her into a lead that passed close to the southern shore of one of the smaller islands. It would provide us with a winter harbour in the shelter on the south side of this unnamed island group.

We anchored Erebus on the twelfth of September, only two days before the freeze up. We lay near the south shore of an island we were to learn was known to the Eskimos as Imnguyaaluk Island. I wanted this to be our shore base well away from the horrors of the three camps in Erebus and Terror bays. It was far far better that no-one would ever know of the terrible end for some of our men there. The drift of the ice river is towards the south, so for the first time since we entered it, we are anchored in a place where the ship is protected from the movement of the ice pressures by the island immediately to our north. It is completely different from our previous location in the ice where it was packing against a lee shore. I am confident the ship is at last safe from ice pressure. I will certainly sleep better now.

Later we had time to explore and map the island group and Captain Fitzjames said that as Commander Gore had named the westernmost Cape after him, it was fitting that this group of islands should be named after me. So they became the Crozier Islands on our charts.

CHAPTER 13

Expedition diary of the first of November 1848
by Captain Crozier

Erebus arrived at Imnguyaaluk Island with fifty nine men aboard and a few months of food stores. Most of this was the condemned tinned food. As soon as the anchor was down and the sails furled I gave an order that was new to me:

'I want fishing lines over the side immediately.' Quite a few of our seamen had worked as fishermen in their lives, so we had experienced men aboard. It proved a very pleasant surprise when they began hauling in a good catch of assorted fish. This proved more than enough to give the entire crew a good filling meal of fresh food. I remarked to Captain Fitzjames;

'James, we have only a few days until the sea freezes and I think this is a golden opportunity to catch as many fish as possible.'

'A capital idea, Francis. Our food problem is so critical that we should have a half of each watch fishing day and night. We can dry the fish for winter food.'

Soon we had about a half of the crew with fishing experience catching fish. Some were splitting and cleaning them and then hanging them on lines in the rigging to dry in the cool winds. Erebus looked more like a fishing boat than a naval ship. It caused quite a bit of amusement amongst the crew.

A little old seaman – Thomas Work from Kirkwall in Orkney - approached me and said:

'Zurr why don't 'ee smoke some o' the fish. We do a lot o' that in the Orkneys to preserve 'em. You'll only need a smoke box and some oak wood chippings to make the smoke.'

'That's a splendid suggestion. But I prefer that you build a small smoke house ashore where the camp is going to be because of the fire risk to the ship. Please go ahead and organise the smoking.'

So within a few days we had a good supply of fresh, dried and smoked fish that was most welcome to our diet. But we still lacked a sufficient food supply to get us through the winter.

Meanwhile, the other half of the crew began the hard labour of preparing the ship for winter quarters – taking down the upper masts, spars and sails and enclosing the deck in canvas. It also included building another shore camp.

We had made a good start with the fish, but we had now to consider hunting the caribou and musk oxen. One man in our crew stood out and became chief hunter for the ship. He had with him three friends and they hunted successfully as a team. One of them was a cabin boy. The man who became our chief hunter was Bosun Thomas Terry and he played a role so important that we were able to survive aboard ship well beyond the time when our stores were exhausted. His story is remarkable and I have asked him write it down for the expedition's diary.

My name is Thomas Terry and I joined the expedition as Bosun aboard Erebus at the age of thirty four years. Although

I was raised in Hackney, I developed an interest in hunting as a boy, when my father and I used to visit the estate of an uncle in Norfolk. There we shot birds, mainly ducks for the pot.

My role as a chief hunter for fresh food for the ship was quite unplanned. It started with my friendship with the ship's dog Neptune and developed after the death of Commander Gore. Commander Gore was a great hunter following a family tradition where his grandfather was a master hunter. As a midshipman aboard Terror on the 1836-37 Arctic expedition led by Captain George Back (later Admiral Sir) he had supplied the officer's mess with a haunch of reindeer for their 1836 Christmas dinner. Commander Gore had brought aboard Erebus the two best hunting rifles that the expedition carried. Happily I was familiar with their use and had had quite a bit of hunting experience. When the surgeons requested a supply of fresh food for the men and condemned the tinned food, there was a need for some good hunters. I was also one of the few aboard who did not like the idea of eating food preserved in tins and had avoided it wherever possible.

If I could hunt then I knew I had the skills to provide fresh food of the kind requested by the doctors. I went along to Captain Fitzjames and explained my past hunting experience and suggested that if I could borrow one of Commander Gore's hunting rifles and train Neptune as a hunting dog, I could provide the ship with a fresh supply of meat as Commander Gore had done. I also explained that with the short rations aboard ship, the best way to keep Neptune alive would be to feed him scraps and offal from the hunting. This could easily be done when the kill was fresh butchered before letting it freeze for transportation back to the ship. Captain Fitzjames readily agreed and I began to spend time away from the ship on hunting trips with Neptune and three friends who were all interested in hunting. We began by bringing in birds.

We had only been at the island for a few days and the crew were busy taking down the upper masts, sails and rigging and getting the ship converted to winter quarters. There were boats ferrying stores and equipment ashore and the upper masts and spars were being floated ashore. Hunting parties had been sent out and we were having some success mainly shooting birds. A small event then occurred that was to have momentous implications for us all and for me in particular.

Soon after the sea froze, a small group of two Eskimo families suddenly appeared and set up their tents on the ice alongside us. It was not long before these small friendly people were aboard and long conversations were taking place. Captain Crozier from his knowledge of Inuktitut learned on previous visits to the Arctic with Parry and Assistant Surgeon Harry Goodsir who had been making a dictionary of Eskimo vocabulary, were our main communicators. But for the rest of us, we just got by with hand signals and smiles. We made gifts of wood and iron to the Eskimos and talked with them about hunting.

Their leader was on older man who proved to be a great hunter. His name was Neeveeovak and he was to become my friend 'NeeVee' and we would hunt together. He indicated to us that it was now the time for hunting tooktoo (that we discovered meant caribou). My father and I had hunted together in Norfolk and I was most keen to participate as our food situation was pretty desperate and we did not have enough to get through the winter. The surgeons had insisted that we needed fresh food and at present we were on very short rations and having to eat the tinned food that had been condemned.

The Captain soon arranged for a joint hunt for tooktoo to take place and eight officers and men including myself left the ship with some sledges of camping gear and an assortment of guns, letting our Eskimo friends guide us. We headed for the mainland and then moved south down the shore. The Captain had told us to keep the party away from the tent at Terror Bay. On the second day we encountered a herd of caribou and our Eskimo friends showed us how they approached them. Our guns were far superior to the bows, arrows and lances of the Eskimos and we had great success killing many caribou, so that blood and bodies decorated the ice all along the coast.

Marine Sergeant Solomon Tozer and I distinguished ourselves with the highest kills. For me, it marked the beginning of what was to become my new permanent role as the ships chief hunter. Everyone was very happy and the carcasses were butchered, the Eskimo making stone covered caches for their meat and the women scraping the skins in preparation for making winter clothing. We butchered our meat and loaded it onto sledges and started taking it back to the ship. There was so much that we had to use the portage method to move it along with us.

We had set up a camp on the shore and here we feasted with the Eskimos. Also present with us in the camp was our ships dog Neptune and he became a great favourite with the Eskimos who had not seen such a dog before. Neevee told us that our dog would be very valuable to us in the winter as he could be used to smell out the snow-covered breathing holes of the bearded seal that was the main food source hunted in winter. Neevee explained that it was the custom for the Eskimos to move out onto the sea ice in winter to live in snow houses or igloos and hunt seals. Here then was the path to our survival also. These simple friendly people had been surviving for centuries in the Arctic and now that we were trapped in their land, our best chance of survival after our stores were exhausted, was to adopt the Eskimo lifestyle.

Captain Crozier was particularly interested because where the ship now lay was at the north end of the hunting area used by the Eskimos and reported by earlier explorers. The land opposite us was a relatively fertile place in summer as shown by the many old tent rings of stone. It was quite different to the more barren lands we had seen to the north including the Cape Felix area.

Neevee explained that there was now little time left before the caribou migrated off King William Island and returned to the American mainland. He said it was necessary for the hunters to move to the south of the island and mentioned a place called Malervalik. Here the sea passage to be crossed is narrowest and it was here that the Eskimos gathered each year to ambush the caribou as they arrived and departed from King William Island. So we set out again on another joint hunt. This time we took twelve men from Erebus and three sledges to move to the south following the North-West Passage taken earlier by the late Commander Gore and his party.

We were gone for several weeks but again the hunting was very good and we cached our meat like the Eskimos did. We roamed a long way south, well past Cape Herschel. One day our hunting took us into Douglas Bay and we came across the remains of a campsite with the large sledge that had been used by Lieutenant Irving and his party that had decided to continue the 1848 retreat. It was on a small island at the head of Douglas Bay and we also found seven graves on the top of the island. There was no sign of the Lieutenant nor the boat and the remaining four men who evidently went with him.

We concluded that they had reached this point and had set up a hunting camp while awaiting the melting of the sea in July. Evidently the hunting was not sufficient and seven men had died, but Lieutenant Irving and his four remaining men had evidently sailed their boat on as had been the original plan of Captain Crozier. Hopefully they had reached Chantrey Inlet (the estuary of Back's Great Fish River) with its reported rich fishing and hunting grounds. Our hopes rose for these gallant few and we wondered how far they had managed to get. Our Eskimo friends were delighted with the wooden sledge and were soon breaking it up for wood for making small sledges, spears and arrows.

By early October the last of the caribou had left the island and Neevee explained that he was next taking his group into the interior of the island to a sacred place called Lake Amitsoq where it was the custom for his people to gather and catch thousands of trout. This and making new clothing from the caribou furs would be their occupation until the middle of winter when they would move out onto the ice to catch seals. We agreed to part and we would sledge our caribou meat supply back to the ship, but if possible I hoped to come out again to fish with my friend. Neevee did his best to describe to me the way to Lake Amitsoq.

CHAPTER 14

Expedition diary of April the tenth 1849
by Captain Crozier

The whole ship was delighted with the success of Bosun Thomas Terry and his small group of hunters. We are a naval expedition trapped in the Arctic ice and our stores all but exhausted. Our retreat had failed dismally. It seems now that we have entered a new stage where our survival will depend on unusual skills possessed by some of the crew and as it turned out by others taught to us by the Eskimos. The best example is of course Bosun Terry. As a successful hunter he developed a friendship with an Eskimo hunter and as a result, our ships dog Neptune became a hunting dog used to smell out the seal breathing holes in winter ice. Bosun Terry and his small hunting group became more and more like their Eskimo friends.

I approved Bosun Terry's request to go out to join his Eskimo friends for fishing at Lake Amitsoq in the interior of King William Island. Not only did they come back with an abundance of fish but they had also obtained full Eskimo clothing. I learned that this was in part because the Bosun had obtained an Eskimo wife at the fishing camp. She had helped make the fur clothing from some of the caribou skins from their joint summer hunt. So when Bosun Terry asked to take his hunters out for winter hunting of seals on the sea ice, I was at first apprehensive but soon agreed. So our hunting team although small was able to supply the ship with fresh fish and meat throughout the year.

I have become friendly with Bosun Terry as I admire his achievement. By adopting the harsh physical life of an Eskimo hunter, he and his small group have become very fit and healthy during their long absences from the ship. In this he has achieved what I had hoped to achieve when I ordered the 1848 summer retreat that failed dismally mainly due to an absence of normal summer weather, poor hunting and the crew's poor physical condition after long spells on short rations.

Bosun Terry and his hunters are today the only crew of Erebus who are fully fit and healthy compared to the half starved condition of those of us who live aboard ship. By the efforts of this small group of men we survive aboard Erebus well beyond the date when our stores finished. I have asked Bosun Terry to write down for the expedition's diary more of his remarkable story of his hunting exploits in winter and of the close relations he has developed with the Eskimos.

It was hard work sledging our caribou meat back to the ship, again using the portage method, but eventually we returned and Captain Crozier and the surgeons were delighted with the fresh supply of food, but it was nowhere near enough to feed fifty nine men for a winter. I went to see Captains Fitzjames and Crozier Crozier and told them about the Eskimo fishing in Lake Amitsoq. I asked if I could take three volunteers and Neptune and go out to seek them and try fishing. I suggested it would be a good chance for Neptune, as we could feed him the fish heads in the same way that my friend NeeVee had told me the Eskimo feed their own dogs.

The idea of leaving the ship in autumn and winter was not popular, as the Arctic night was fast closing in and there was a good chance that we might get lost and not find the Eskimo or the lake. It was this hesitation by most of the crew that gave me my long term hunting team. Able Seaman Charlie Best and George Thompson stepped forward. Ships boy David Young who had come on the southern hunt also was very keen to come. He had grown into a tall long legged young man and we found he could run like the wind and was fast becoming a good shot. Charlie and Bill proved to be very hard workers and could butcher an animal or clean fish and pack them into skin sacks very rapidly.

We were offering a chance of increasing the food supply, so after some brief discussion between the Captains, permission was given. It was a sad parting for many of our friends who did not think that we would return.

There followed a wild adventure for us, where we learned very much about the Eskimo way of life and became much like the Eskimos ourselves. We took with us short rations for two weeks only but none of the tins of food. We decided to follow the coast back to the south where we had left NeeVee and his group, before turning inland so as to try to follow the route to Lake Amitsoq.

It was Neptune who found the Eskimos and the lake at a time when our food was exhausted and we thought we were lost. We set up our tent amongst the Eskimo groups. We enquired for NeeVee and soon there as a joyous reunion. However for us wearing our european clothes and boots and living in a thin canvas tent, the autumn weather proved very cold and the winds very strong. Fortunately we had brought with us trade items and gifts for the Eskimo. Some wood and iron and a few knives, but the most popular of our items were the steel sewing needles for the women, also glass beads. There were also plenty of iron fish hooks for the men. With these items we were each of us able to trade for new fur Eskimo clothing and boots with some spare skins for bedding. We had earlier given our caribou skins to NeeVee and he thought it was very amusing to trade them back again but as new clothing.

As we settled in amongst the Eskimos we slowly learned their language. At the social gatherings in the evenings I found myself popular with the Eskimo men and especially with the women. I must explain that I am a large man and a head and shoulders taller than the Eskimos. But what interested them most about me was my hair. By European standards I am hairy with a beard and long hair, as most of us have these days. However it was my body hair that fascinate them. I was often asked to open my shirt and the Eskimos, who lack such body hair, would comment on my hairy chest. Both the men and the women liked to stroke the hair as though I was a pet animal. It fascinated them.

One thing led to another and one day NeeVee presented me with his oldest daughter as a wife. Her name is Yuka meaning 'Bright Star'. She was a charming and hard-working woman and an excellent seamstress and proud of the fur clothes she made for us. She spent days chewing our furs to make them soft and comfortable to wear. So I became a member of NeeVee's family. But I explained to him that I would not take her back to the ship with me because we were only men there, and they had not seen women for many years and there would be trouble. He agreed and we settled the matter when I promised that I would join him and his small band as often as I could.

We spent much of our days fishing, but we took time off to build ourselves a windproof house near the lake. We did this simply by digging a cave into a bank of dry gravel and then fronting it with a wall of fitted stones, and a small, low skin-covered entrance. We called it Fish House and it came to *play a big role in our lives over the following years. It got a reputation for moving around, because all of us trying to find it when travelling back from the ship, experienced difficulties. Once the house was sealed, we set up an oil lamp made from an old tin with oil traded from the Eskimos and so we had light and some warmth inside in the increasingly long hours of darkness.*

We had, to all intents and purposes, become Eskimos. Most days we had Eskimo visitors who studied our stone wall with interest. Daily we exchanged small gifts with them – those fish hooks and needles lasted a long time. We were also invited into the tents of the Eskimos, for many had not encountered white men before. They were curious to learn about us and our great ships and why we were so rich in iron and wood – things that were extremely scarce in their world. But there was very much for us to learn in order to survive in this frozen hostile land. The Eskimos all stored their killed food in stone caches, where it froze and was preserved for many months and even years. It was their law that one man could never touch the cache of another man however lacking in food he might be, for to do so could easily cause the starvation of the cache owner and his family. So we followed suit and put this vital law into practice.

Hardest for us was gaining the confidence and ability to travel long distances and navigate in the Arctic night. The solution should have been obvious if we had thought about it, but again it was the Eskimos who showed us the way. Apart from the intense cold and the need to build an igloo or snow house when the winds get up, winter travel can be straightforward using moonlight. In fact to travel by Arctic moonlight in the winter, when the winds are light, is a wonderful experience. The moonlight is reflected off the snow and the landscape is almost as clear as daylight. Overhead the star-studded sky and the beauty of the Milky Way can be stunning and then there are the northern lights which can be most spectacular and colourful. We became experts in quickly being able to build ourselves an igloo or snow house when the weather became violent. Unlike summer travel there are no meltwater pools and soft mud to hamper one's progress.

In January the Eskimos, now resplendent in their new winter clothing, moved offshore onto the sea ice where they spread out in small groups and built igloos. From these with their dogs, they would hunt the bearded seal at his air hole. This amounted to using the dogs to locate the breathing hole and then sitting there with infinite patience and a lance with a harpoon on a line, awaiting the appearance of the seal. We had cached a great deal of trout for collection by sledge in the spring and returned to the ship with our sledges loaded with frozen fish. Our arrival at the ship in the dark of winter with a load of frozen fish, wearing new fur clothing caused a sensation and great joy. Our promise of a lot more frozen fish in the spring caused great delight, for most had given us up for dead.

But it was time now for seal hunting and our Eskimo friends were now scattering out onto the sea ice. On the shore of Imnguyaaluk Island, adjacent to the ship the crew had built a winter camp and storehouse. With the now-enthusiastic support of Captain Fitzjames, we were permitted to move there to try our hand at seal hunting. We moved there next and then we four hunters and Neptune set out to go seal hunting, as best as we could understand it from the words of NeeVee. Here again we were very lucky because far out on the ice we met another group of friendly Eskimo and they built us an ice house.

One of them took us seal hunting and helped us train Neptune to find the breathing holes. Neptune soon became our tool for finding the breathing holes, once he realised that *we would reward him with a piece of seal as soon as we had killed one. We began to bring in a number of seals. We hunters who lived mainly off the ship with the Eskimos became adept at eating seal meat which we often cooked on seal blubber fires at the shore camp. Back on board the ship seal meat was not a favourite, but as there was insufficient food, it as a case of take it or leave it.*

Some of the seamen were not at all complimentary in their remarks when they saw us dressed like Eskimos and learning their ways. Some thought it primitive and savage, but there was no alternative to a slow death by starvation than in effect to become Eskimos ourselves. We managed to survive that winter, and when the spring came we organised a sledge party for the long haul back to Fish House to collect our frozen stocks of trout.

CHAPTER 15

Expedition diary continued by Captain Crozier
in August 1849

With the freezing of the sea in winter 1848-49, we were trapped for our fourth successive winter and as our provisions supplied us only for three years, they were all but exhausted except for an abundance of the condemned tinned food. As winter closed in I called a meeting of officers in the great cabin.

It was an extremely sombre meeting, for our food supplies were inadequate for another winter despite the successes of our fishermen and our hunters with their new Eskimo friends. The meeting reviewed the dismal failure of the retreat to the south, a retreat that had clearly demonstrated that our expedition was not going to escape by marching out to escape the ice trap which had caught us. I continued the meeting by saying:

'There is only one slight hope, which is the discovery by the hunters that Lieutenant Irving with a party of four men had survived in Douglas Bay until the sea in Simpson Strait had thawed. This small group appears to have abandoned their sledge and left surplus camping equipment with the seven graves. They probably then sailed off into Chantrey Inlet, the estuary of Back's Great Fish River, famous for is good fishing and hunting. We can guess that they were near starving, but it is hoped that their hunting and fishing fortunes changed. There is a slim chance that some of these few might get to a Hudson's Bay outpost and alert the Admiralty to our position. If they succeed then we might expect a rescue party to arrive here at about this time.'

This was received with gloomy looks but I continued:

'If Lieutenant Irving does not get through to a Hudson's Bay outpost then the admiralty, who no doubt have parties out searching for us, will not know where we are.'

'It is extremely unfortunate that we didn't leave a record of our achievements up Wellington Channel and our proposed route to the south or south-west on Beechey Island,' said Captain Fitzjames.

Lieutenant Fairholme added: 'The admiralty will know that our three-year food supply has expired by now.'

'Everyone was so confident in London before we left that no plans were made for a possible retreat. They will not know if we will retreat north or south. Or that our retreat failed so dismally because of an abnormally cold year,' I said.

Lieutenant Fairholme then suggested: 'It seems essential that we try to communicate with the admiralty. Our only hope here is that in this year's summer thaw we send a boat of volunteers north to back track our route to Lancaster Sound and try to find some whaling ships'.

I added: 'If Erebus is not released, it will mean another year in the ice on a starvation diet mainly depending on our hunters for food.'

Lieutenant Fairholme replied: 'It cannot be helped as there are no alternatives. In fact I will volunteer to make the attempt if I can have seven volunteers with me to man one of the whale boats.'

I looked carefully at this officer. He is physically the largest of our officers and a man confident in his strength and ability. If anyone is to lead such a desperate venture then there could be no better man. So I replied: 'A very courageous offer Lieutenant but you know that there will probably be no turning back. We will be working Erebus further south to try to reach the summer open-water channel along the north coast of the American continent. A boat might not find us.'

'Thank you, Captain Crozier, but I am aware of that. I have no plans to return to the ship. We go on the understanding that we either get home or die in the attempt. It may prove that Lady Jane Sound will not be open when we get there. So we shall carry two small sledges with us in case we have to travel by foot for the second part of the journey.'

I added: 'Should that prove the case then I suggest that you cross Somerset Land into Prince Regent Inlet and make for Fury Beach. The stores have been there for more than two decades, but something might be left that can help you and I believe there are boats there. Sir John Ross took three away with him and left some others. There is a possibility to repeat his escape.'

Ice Master Thomas Blanky then spoke: 'As you know I was with Sir John Ross on that expedition and the retreat. I can go over the charts with you to show you the route we took and also the route used by Sir James Clark Ross when he sledged to and from Prince Regent Inlet to King William Land as it was then called.'

'Thank you Thomas, that will be a great help,' replied Lieutenant Fairholme.

Captain Fitzjames added: 'If you succeed James, then the Admiralty might learn that Erebus is still occupied in autumn 1849. So the earliest relief expedition might reach us in summer 1850.'

And so it came to pass, in July 1849, Lieutenant Fairholme and a crew of seven men left Erebus as soon as leads appeared in the summer breakup of the ice. They headed north. There were very few leads and none near the ship. It was an emotional send off for everyone as the surviving crew took this last opportunity to send mail to their loved ones. Practically everyone turned out to lend them a hand to drag the whale boat, stores and sledges across the five miles of unbroken ice to reach the nearest open lead. We cheered them as they set off. Fairholme and his crew looked very small and alone as they rowed away from us into the white wilderness, but they carried our hopes of rescue. But it also meant that our numbers aboard ship had now been reduced to fifty one men.

For the fifty one of us who remained aboard Erebus, there were no leads any nearer to the ship that summer and we were too few and too weak to cut a channel five miles long through the ice. So we remained aboard Erebus, fast in the ice and we resigned ourselves to a fifth year in the ice on starvation rations. We were now wholly dependent on our fishing and on the success of our hunters for survival.

CHAPTER 16

Expedition diary written on April the tenth 1850
by Captain James Fitzjames

This is Captain James Fitzjames taking over the writing of the diary for the expedition following the untimely death of our second expedition leader Captain Francis Crozier. I will say a few words of introduction first.

I joined the Royal Navy in August 1825, and served in various ships. In 1835 I joined an expedition led by Colonel Chesney to see if the River Euphrates was navigable by steamers and could be used for a route to India. This involved disassembling two steamers and transporting the sections across the Syrian desert to the river, to reassemble them and then descending the river. The two steamers were assembled and set out. One was wrecked and the other, on which I was mate, completed the passage, and provided a valuable experience in steam engines. I next served in H.M.S. Ganges on operations to bombard the coastal fortresses of Mehemet Ali in Lebanon and Syria.

In May 1841 I went to China in H.M.S. Cornwallis to fight in the Chinese opium wars. There I commanded a rocket brigade in several engagements and was wounded during the capture of Ching-Kiang-Foo. In 1842 I was promoted to the rank of Commander and joined H.M.S. Clio until October 1844. With the death of Sir John Franklin in spring 1846 and of Captain Crozier in spring

1850, I have now assumed leadership of the expedition. But we remain trapped in the ice river with only one ship.

There was no release for Erebus in summer 1849 and most of the men grew weaker on the very short rations. Some became very despondent. Everyone was now thin and hungry except for the small party of four hunters who had become like Eskimos, adopting their dress and customs and living off the ship for long periods of time. They brought in seals in the winter, caribou and birds in the summer and fish in the late summer and early winter. But there was never an abundance of food and we had to eak out our food with the now feared tins of cooked food that had been condemned by the surgeons.

On the seventh of April 1850, Captain Crozier died. It was again the mysterious illness that led to the suffocating death. We had been sparingly using the now hated tins of food together with whatever the hunters could bring in and whatever we could trade with infrequent Eskimo visitors. Although very sad, his death was not a surprise, for we were still plagued by outbreaks of the suffocating disease, and knew the necessary risks of eating the tinned food. Since being at Imnguyaaluk Island, we had lost another five men this way including Captain Crozier, and with the departure of Lieutenant Fairholme and seven men by boat to the north in summer 1849, our numbers are now reduced to forty six men.

However we accorded Captain Crozier the most fitting military funeral possible. He was buried on the south-east end of Imnguyaaluk Island. This is another of those bleak flat gravel shores similar to where we had buried Sir John Franklin and Commander Gore. The only difference here is that the gravel ridges on the south of the island run east to west.

Almost all of the crew attended the funeral. I read the service. A wooden coffin was prepared and a wooden headboard carved with his details. The grave was made in a fissure in the ground that was afterwards sealed with cement, brought for use about the ships steam engine. The surviving Royal Marines provided an honour guard and fired volleys over the grave. It was a very sad occasion as it was another demonstration that we were unlikely to escape the ice trap.

If nobody ever escaped, what would become of our vast scientific records? Many of these had been buried at the Depot Camp at Victory Point just before the 1848 disastrous retreat. What would become of the hard won information of the channels and islands we had charted, of the magnetic data and the fauna, flora and geology carefully recorded? Abandoned ships would eventually sink for want of pumping, so storage ashore was the best hope. I had therefore suggested that alongside Captain Crozier's grave we should prepare a vault in the ground. In this we could deposit copies of some of the records of the expedition to date.

In order to keep the records dry from the summer melt-water they would be sealed in metal cylinders and these would be placed in a vault in the ground. The vault would be sealed by lining it with cement. The ships had both carried a supply of cement for working around the steam engines and insulating their fires from the wooden hulls. This was duly done. A number of Eskimos attended the ceremony and were impressed when some of the papers blew away in the wind and when the volleys of musket fire rolled out.

Afterwards we returned to the ship where I read myself in as the new leader of the expedition. But I had become the third leader of the now very much reduced remains of this former grand enterprise.

CHAPTER 17

Expedition diary for the twentieth of April 1850
by Captain James Fitzjames

With the death of our much respected second leader Captain Crozier, most of the surviving old Terror hands decided that they could no longer wait for Erebus to break free. The Terror men were very close to their captain and had never fitted in as one with the Erebus crew. What we on Erebus had seen as Captain Crozier's gloomy predictions had proved all too correct. His crew probably remembered that Captain Crozier's advice to either keep out of the ice river or put in only one ship, had been overruled by Sir John Franklin acting with my enthusiastic support.

A meeting was held in the great cabin. Ice Master Thomas Blanky spoke first:

'Captain Fitzjames I thank you for calling this meeting. Since Captain Crozier died, the remainder of us Terror men have been talking about another attempt to march and sail out of here. We realise that we're physically weak after the years on short rations and we'll not be able to get the 1200 miles to the Hudson's Bay outposts on the Great Slave Lake. But if the weather is better than in 1848, we think we can get further than we did at that time.'

Lieutenant George Hodgson then spoke:

'We're thinking of attempting to march and sail to Repulse Bay or Iwillik as the Eskimos call it. This would mean travelling to the south of King William Island or even Chantry Inlet and then turning east. The total distance will be about 450 miles. The objective is to hopefully find a whaling ship.'

Marine Sergeant Solomon Tozer then spoke:

'Captain, some of the marines and myself would like to make this attempt. We cannot face another year of waiting on near starvation food in case the ship is freed from the ice.'

'Very well, men,' I replied. 'I have no objections to any who want to leave and wish you well. But it is still my belief that we have a chance to sail Erebus out of here if only we can get free of the ice. Please go away now and decide amongst yourselves who will go and who will stay'.

The next day I was considerably shaken to learn that thirty one men – the majority Terror men – had decided to march out in the coming summer. They would take one whale boat on a sledge heading for Repulse Bay (Iwillik). The party would be led by Ice Master Blanky, Lieutenant Hodgeson and Marine Sergeant Solomon Tozer and would include Terror's Assistant Surgeon Alexander Macdonald. Marine William Pilkington of Erebus decided to accompany them.

The party would be thirty one men, leaving Erebus with only fifteen men including one officer – myself. This would be barely enough to handle the ship. I requested that before they departed it would considerably help those who were to remain if they would assist us in completing the work of re-rigging Erebus after her winter quarters in case she was able to break out.

So May the first 1850 was a very sad day as the thirty one men departed Erebus, knowing we would probably never see our friends again. A few of us who will remain, including myself, walked along with them a short way, but turned back when they started to cross the partly melted sea ice. Their expectation after the 1848 retreat, was not to travel more than a few miles per day. The health and strength of the men was not good after five years mainly living on short rations and a few men had the blackened gums of scurvy for our lemon juice had run out two years before.

Ice Master Blanky and Marine Sergeant Solomon Tozer both carried shotguns and marched ahead of the boat and sledge. We stood on the shoreline and watched them move away. They had raised a canvas sail on the mast of the boat to assist the sledge team. This dwindled until we saw no more of them.

A LETTER WRITTEN IN PENCIL ON THE FLYLEAF OF A POCKET BIBLE BY LIEUTENANT GEORGE HENRY HODGSON OF H.M.S. TERROR IN SEPTEMBER 1850. FOUND NEAR THE FALLS AT THE MOUTH OF BACK'S GREAT FISH RIVER.

Dear Mother and Father,

This is a brief account to let you know how things have ended with us, for the entire expedition seems to be lost. The ships were trapped in an ice river in 1846 and have not escaped. Sir John Franklin died in 1847 and Captain Crozier in 1850. We tried several times to escape but were not successful. Today our numbers are reduced to only fifteen still aboard ship including Captain Fitzjames and a scatter of survivors from the thirty one of us (mainly Terror men) who left the ship last month in a final attempt to escape. We took only one boat on a large sledge and a smaller sledge with camping gear. We planned to head for Repulse Bay, that is some 450 miles from the ship.

We met a few families of Eskimo near Washington Bay and proceeded on south, but the sea ice had become too much melted to walk across and yet the ice breakup had not yet occurred.

When we reached the narrows of Simpson Strait, our party split into two. Fifteen of us remained with the boat awaiting the sea ice to break up. The other sixteen men led by Marine Sergeant Solomon Tozer and Ice Master Thomas Blanky decided to march on across the south of King William Island. They carried with them the inflatable Halkett boat. After two weeks of poor hunting we were at last able to launch the boat. We then crossed onto the mainland of the Adelaide Peninsula and camped. We left seven men there as they were too weak to continue.

Eight of us were able to sail the boat and work her along the coast to what we thought was Chantry Inlet. Imagine our disappointment when we discovered that we had made an error and entered a long creek by mistake. It was heart breaking because most of the men were too weak to go on. So we overturned the boat right on the low shoreline to make a shelter. We all slept well wrapped up under the boat.

Six of the men were weak and there were only two of us who were still able to walk any distance, myself and Able Seaman William Wentzall. I decided to split us up. I would set out for the Eskimo settlement described by George Back at the falls at the mouth of Back's Great Fish River to purchase food and organise help. William Wentzall would remain with the boat and a good supply of guns, ammunition and powder to hunt for the party. I was also anxious that a metal box we had brought with us which contained copies of the precious records of the expedition, be looked after.

So early one morning I set out looking for Chantry Inlet which I soon found and then followed its shoreline to the south. There I was able to catch fish in the sea. Living off fish I have reached the falls at the mouth of Back's Great Fish River and met a group of Eskimos who lived there. I was astonished to find them hostile and not at all friendly. I had never met this before with these normally friendly people. They took away my equipment and put me into an empty tent where I have now been for two days. They have not brought me any food or drink. At this rate I will not last more than a few days. I wonder at the cause of this unusual hostile behaviour from these normally friendly people. There seems no possibility of organising any rescue bid for the men left at the boat.

Goodbye and God Bless you both,

Your Affectionate Son,

Lieutenant George Henry Hodgson.

A LAST LETTER WRITTEN IN PENCIL ON THE FLYLEAF OF A BOOK OF PRAYER BY TERROR ICE MASTER THOMAS BLANKY IN SEPTEMBER 1850 TO HIS WIFE. FOUND ON THE TODD ISLETS IN A GROUP OF FIVE BODIES.

My dearest Esther, It grieves me to write this last message to you to tell you that I am not able to get home. We have been impossibly trapped in the ice now for four years. It is a remote place so very far for anywhere. But I want you to know that it was not for want of trying. I am sitting on the top of a small islet (Todd Islets) off the south coast of what we have proved to be King William Island. Both our ships are trapped in the ice to the north of us and we have abandoned them – twice as it happens.

The expedition went extremely well for the first two years and we explored new channels and saw a frozen Polar Sea. Amazingly in summer 1846 we found an open seaway that connected with the summer open water channel along the northern margin of the American continent. It is an open water North-West Passage. But it has many reefs and shallows and Terror went aground on one of these and was got off in sinking condition. But she was repaired by great efforts made by the crews of both ships. Although no use to our deep draft ships, we think the Passage is suitable for small ships and boats only. It lies to the east of King William Island. I am looking south now across the open-water channel that borders the north coast of the American continent.

As we were unable to use the open-water passage in summer 1846, Sir John Franklin led both ships into a great ice river that filled a strait that Graham Gore had mapped as a second North-West Passage, this one lying to the west of King William Island. Neither I nor Captain Crozier nor Ice Master Reid wanted to do this, but Sir John decided otherwise. We might have succeeded but the summer of 1847 cannot really be described as a summer but rather a continuation of winter. As a result the ships were not released and Terror was thrown over onto her beam ends by ice pressure. Both crews wintered aboard Erebus over winter 1847-48.

When I wrote to you last from Disko Island I said the crossing of the Arctic might take us as long as seven years. I may have been right, but at that time we thought we carried more than ample food stores with us that we might even stretch to seven years if need be. Unfortunately some of the tinned food proved to be tainted or poisoned and we lost too many officers and men to its effects that are horrible - a creeping paralysis that ends in suffocation. We also lost a lot of our food stores to lighten the ship when Terror went aground in the Matty Islands and could not go back for them as the ship was in a sinking condition.

By spring 1848 we had only a few months supply of food left, so Captain Crozier ordered a land retreat to the south. He wanted to get us into an area of good hunting where we could recover from the short rations. Dease and Simpson had reported the south part of King William Land to be abounding in caribou and musk oxen. We set out and the abnormally cold weather with snowstorms and gales and without any signs of summer proved our downfall. Also the men were not strong and the heavy loads proved too much for them. We barely made it to the summer hunting grounds, but were too early in the year for successful hunting for the 105 men on the retreat.

A half of us returned to re-man Erebus. Surprisingly she was released by the ice a few weeks later and we worked her south to the shelter of some islands off the western cape of King William Island. But we were too late to save the half of the men that had been left behind. My friend James Reid had volunteered to stay with a boat load of Erebus sick. All the men had died of starvation when the hunting failed. Captain Crozier anchored Erebus off one of the islands off the western cape and would not let anyone visit the sick camps we had left, except himself and Assistant Surgeons Harry Goodsir and Alexander Macdonald.

We were two years in the ice off that island, but happily were befriended by the Eskimos and went on joint hunting trips with them for caribou in summer and seals in winter. A group of our men led by Bosun Thomas Terry became successful hunters. They kept us alive but on very short rations. Captain Crozier died earlier this year. Soon after this, Lieutenant Hodgson, Royal Marine Sergeant Solomon Tozer and myself led a group of thirty one men (mainly from Terror) in a last attempt to reach Repulse Bay. But for most of us the journey has proved too much.

Half way down the west coast of King William Island we divided into two parties. George Hodgson and fourteen men stopped with the wooden boat to hunt and await the melting of the sea before sailing to the American mainland. Marine Sergeant Solomon Tozer and I in a party of the sixteen remaining men marched along the south shore of King William Island. We carried an inflatable Halkett boat with us to cross open water channels. Here at the Todd Islets several men became too weak to continue because of lack of food. A decision was taken. The men who will march on with Solomon Tozer will eat the dead. Those of us who refuse will stay here with me and probably die.

I have four companions with me and we have had no food for a week now. We are good friends and shipmates. We are thin and terribly hungry but have been so for a long time now. Surprisingly there is a certain humour in our situation here. For we have with us a single unopened tin of pemmican – a rich meat and fat mixture that is very nourishing. We have it on the ground in front of us and it amuses us to talk about it. You see some of the tins of food that we brought with us carry a deadly poison. It causes a prolonged and horrible death finally by suffocation.

There were no problems with the tinned food in the first year but a whole sledging party from Erebus led by Commander Graham Gore were the first to be taken ill and most died. Yet a second sledge party from Terror, travelling with them was unaffected. Many men died in this manner over the winter of 1847 – 48 and the surgeons condemned the tinned food that put us all on extremely short rations. However over the years since it has been necessary to eat this food and others died of the suffocating illness. These included Captain Crozier only a month ago. So we sit together, good friends, united in our determination never to resort to cannibalism and look at our one remaining tin of pemmican and talk about it.

But none of us wish to die by the slow suffocating death. So the tin remains unopened. We are afraid to open and eat it. Rather a cruel final joke for us in this desolate land. We are now too weak to go on and will probably die quietly here. We came to this islet that we might last look across a sea channel to the distant coast of the American continent. That is where our countrymen live but we cannot reach them because we are still 1000 miles from the nearest Hudson's Bay Company outposts.

I send my love to you Esther and my best wishes to your relatives. Remember me to our friends. I doubt that this letter will ever be found, but stranger things have happened. All my love and Goodby. Thomas.

LETTER WRITTEN IN PENCIL IN A DIARY BY ROYAL MARINE SERGEANT SOLOMON TOZER TO HIS PARENTS IN SUMMER 1851

My dear parents,

I write this as a loving farewell to you, for although six long years have passed since we parted when I sailed with Sir John Franklin, it is now certain that I will not return home to you. Our great expedition has become a great disaster and most of the men are dead and the ships abandoned. My own fate appears clear, for I am alone in a tent, where I was brought by the Kinepatoo Eskimos who inhabit this area. But they are not feeding me and I was weak to begin with and my powder expended. They are distrustful of strangers and I think they desire the few things that I still have with me. It is unlikely that this message will ever reach you, but it is my wish to write a record of how hard we fought for our lives in our hope to get home to our families again.

The first two years of the expedition were a great success and we explored two new straits, proved Cornwallis and King William Lands were in fact islands and not peninsulas. We also discovered an open-water North-West Passage suitable for small ships but not deep enough for our two big ships. Lieutenant Gore led a sledge party that mapped the last 100 mile stretch of another North-West Passage but it is ice filled. Sir John Franklin decided to take the ships through this passage and then on to Bering Strait. Once we entered the ice field we never left it. Summer 1847 was very cold and the ships were not released. Instead our ship Terror was thrown over onto her port side by ice pressure. We abandoned the ships in summer 1848 but the retreat was a failure. About a half of us got back to H.M.S. Erebus.

Soon after our return Erebus was released and we worked her south to where we had left the sick half of the expedition. We had hoped they would be alive because of summer hunting. But the hunting had evidently failed and they had died of starvation. Captain Crozier kept the ship at Imnguyaaluk Island away from the camps where the men died. We lived there for two years very poorly. In summer 1849 Lieutenant Fairholme left with a boat of volunteers to retrace our route and try to contact some whaling ships. At the island we met friendly Eskimos and went hunting with them for caribou in summer and seals in winter. But the hunting could not provide for fifty one men and we had to eak out the supplies with the tinned food, some of which was poisoned and men continued to die. Captain Crozier died this way in spring 1850.

This was a great blow for us Terror men as we thought most highly of Captain Crozier. He had tried his best to prevent the ships from entering the ice river where we became trapped. But he was overruled by Sir John Franklin supported by Commander Fitzjames. Soon after our captain's death most of us from Terror decided to leave the ship in a last attempt to reach Repulse Bay and hopefully some whaling ships. Ice master Thomas Blanky started it by saying 'Let's go home boys. I've had enough of waiting around here for the ice to open up and I don't like the food'

A party of thirty one of us mainly from Terror set out in May 1850 with one boat and a sledge and camping gear. We had one interesting encounter with four families of Eskimos as we marched south along the south-west coast of King William Island. We were making surprisingly good progress following the smooth ice near the shore and with the strong north-westerly wind pushing the boat sail to help us. We had been able to shoot some birds that we hung on the gunnels of the boat. It was on the tenth day of the march and we were coming to the south end of a large bay (Washington Bay) when we espied some Eskimo families on the shore. This was an important encounter for us as we wished to trade for fresh food.

Two men awaited us at the shoreline, so I approached them accompanied by Erebus Royal Marine William Pilkington. They were obviously uncertain of us and so I asked Marine Pilkington to lay his musket on the ground and I approached them alone. I tried greeting them but have little knowledge of their language. So I beckoned Pilkington to join me. The two Eskimos seemed to understand that we meant them no harm. So Pilkington and I walked around the ice crack and joined them. We repeated the greetings and I took out a knife and dug into the ice trying to make a hole like the seals do to breath. I also scratched the outline of a seal on the ice to try to turn the conversation to seal meat, but I do not think they understood. So I opened my mouth and mimicked putting handfuls of food into it. I think they understood that. Then I tried to explain that our ship had been turned over onto her side in the ice and we were on our way to Iwillik or Repulse Bay on our way home.

By then the boat and sledges had passed us and the men were setting up a camp on a small cape to the south. The other Eskimos arrived also. I was desperate to get some fresh seal meat for the men who were weak and hungry. So I went to their packs and opened them looking for seal meat. They gave me enough to fill a pack and we put it on a dogs back and went to our camp. There I got the men to raise their arms into the air, palms outward, to show that they were unarmed. As communications were poor I asked Assistant Surgeon Alexander Macdonald, who had some knowledge of their language, to try communicating.

While our campsite was being prepared some of the men had gone to a nearby lake and caught a salmon. So with that and the seal meat we had a fair meal that night. The Eskimo women had put up their skin tents and so I went back to them. I brought presents with me in the form of the knife, some coins and large beads for the ladies that were accepted. I hoped it would lead to further trade for more seal meat as the seal hunting season was ending with the ice melting and the Eskimos would have caches of seal meat scattered about. I then entered a tent and was given water to drink that was very welcome. I pulled out my notebook and made a few sketches and wrote a few notes about the Eskimos and their names.

We then turned in for the night. I was awoken early the next morning by sounds of the Eskimo dogs moving their sledges. As I went outside I called to them to stop and tried to ask again for seal meat. But they were evidently in a hurry and did not stop. This was a big disappointment for us, but I guess the few Eskimos were afraid of our large numbers and food shortage and did not wish to put themselves at risk as their lifestyle is precarious at best.

Some days later, Lieutenant Hodgson decided to remain on the shore with the boat and fourteen men to hunt and await the thaw before sailing on. Ice Master Thomas Blanky and myself and fourteen men decided to continue on along the coast of King William Island. We brought the inflatable Halkett boat with us. Hunting was poor and we again divided on the south coast. A few of the men had decided that the only way to carry on was to eat the dead. The others led by Ice Master Thomas Blanky refused to do this and decided they could go no further. So we parted.

I led the group that were to live by eating the dead (I will not give names) although I refused to do this. We took the Halkett boat. Some weeks afterwards we were reduced to only four of us, and were on the ice approaching the Boothian Peninsula. I was only skin and bones and weak with hunger. There we met some Eskimos who fed us and befriended us. One of our men died shortly afterwards of an illness but this friendly Eskimo named Tooshooartthariu looked after us and fed us all winter and throughout the next spring of 1851. I was able to recover fully and tried to repay our Eskimos friends by hunting for them with my gun. I killed many animals and birds.

One of our men died that summer when he fell into the sea from a small ice floe he was using to cross a lead. I decided it was time for the last two of us to march south for the Hudson's Bay post at Fort Churchill. Our Eskimo friend Tooshooarthariu arranged for another Eskimo to accompany us to the post. So the three of us carrying the Halkett boat set out for the south. I tried to give a gun to our friend Tooshooarthariu but he was afraid of it. So I gave him my sword instead – he called it a long knife.

It was a tough summer journey with much water on the ice and melting snow and streams on the land. I am sorry to say we lost my last western companion in another accident crossing a lead in the ice. Finally a month later my Eskimo guide and I arrived in the Chesterfield area where the fierce Kinnapatoo Eskimos live. There, as strangers, we were captured by a hunting band who killed my Eskimo companion. They were interested in my gun although I was out of powder and ammunition. They took me to their camp and placed me inside a tent where I remain without any food. It looks as though I am a prisoner and that I will not be able to escape to Fort Churchill. So I write this last message as my record of six years of struggle in the far north. I send you my love and say goodbye.

Your loving son Solomon Tozer

CHAPTER 18

Expedition diary for the twentieth of May 1850
by Captain Fitzjames

Since May 1850 the ship seems empty after the thirty one, mainly Terror men left us hauling one boat on a sledge with a second sledge carrying camping gear and the inflatable Halkett boat. After five years in the ice the great Franklin expedition of 1845 is now reduced to one ship - Erebus - occupied by one officer (myself) and fourteen men. Terror was last seen in 1848 still lying on her port side with a pressure ridge hard against her bottom holding her stable in that position. Aboard her, the bunks were occupied by the bodies of the officers and men we lost to the food poisoning in winter 1847-48.

Our supplies had been for three years only and are almost all long gone. We ran out of rum, lemon juice, candles, and fuel for lanterns two years ago. We burn wood only in the cooking stove today and keep the last few tons of coal for our long-awaited breakout from this place. Perhaps most bizarre is our food supply. We are dependent on fishing and hunting for food. The local Eskimos are friendly and we have hunted jointly with them, learning many of their skills.

Commander Graham Gore was our best hunter, but he did not survive the tinned food poisoning. Today a group of hunters has emerged centred on Bosun Thomas Terry and three helpers. The departure of thirty one men has increased our survival chances aboard Erebus because our hunters will now be feeding only fifteen men instead of forty six.

I have impressed upon the few men left that our best chances are still to remain with the ship and hope we can break her out of the ice in the thaw this summer. If so we can still reach the summer open-water channel along the northern margin of the American continent. On the late Captain Crozier's orders we had abandoned the ships in 1848 only to return after achieving a retreat of only 100 miles. By great good fortune Erebus was released in the summer thaw of 1848 but not in that of 1849. Will July 1850 bring another release?

Our living conditions aboard ship are now exceedingly primitive and not at all like that of a Royal Navy ship. We no longer have fuel to waste and so have a wood fire only once a day for cooking and making water. The hot water heating system has been off now for over a year. Our candles and oils are gone and we use seal blubber oil lamps of our own making.

Seal blubber produces blubber soot that impregnates everything. The crew look terrible. Emaciated men with long hair and beards with bodies and clothing impregnated with black blubber soot. My own appearance is greatly different from when we departed London. I am today a tall but thinner man and like the crew I have let my beard grow, although I trim mine in naval fashion and try to keep up appearances. This is important as our lives depend on my holding the crew together with naval discipline.

The crew no longer look like the Royal Navy, but rather like a group of vagabond castaways living in what used to be a Royal Navy ship. However they enjoy camping ashore when the weather permits and have good relations with our hunters. Unlike the hunters the men have not yet learned to eat raw meat, but still prefer to cook it usually over blubber stoves of our own making. I am pleased that they have some off-ship interest, as I don't want them too idle and depressed. The upkeep of the ship and the unrigging and rerigging for winter quarters keeps us pretty busy in the ten months each year when the ice is solid.

Today we regret not having had time to bring the spare clothing back on board from the Depot Camp on our return in 1848. We put it ashore as a part of the depot camp in case both ships were lost to ice pressures. But on our return from the 1848 retreat we only had a few weeks to rerig Erebus and get the stores back aboard. We all lack changes of clothing and what we have is worn, torn and dirty. We are a ship of ragged scarecrows. The only exception is the group of four men who are the hunters led by Bosun Thomas Terry. These men are fit and healthy and dress in Eskimo fur clothing which they have purchased during their long absences from the ship. Although they are now more Eskimo than Royal Navy seamen, we are dependent on them for our main food source.

The responsibility for the ship and her navigation weighs heavily on me. If anything should happen to me as the last officer with navigation skills the ship is lost. Our chances of getting through this ice-filled North-West Passage decrease every time our numbers are reduced. We can take no more losses as we are now far fewer than is needed to properly work the ship in the ocean. However for getting through the calm waters of the ice field, we are just enough to work the ship. Right now our lives are a gamble and probably dependent on getting away further south in the thaw this coming July.

Yesterday I was lying in my bunk to keep warm, when I heard three loud cheers from the crew and went up on deck to see what was the cause. I found all the remaining crew on deck surrounding a single Eskimo who looked terrified. I realised that of course the crew with their blubber-soot blackened faces and oily clothing and thin pinched faces with bushy beards and long greasy hair looked most frightening to him.

So I ordered the men below and tried to calm the frightened Eskimo. It is very important to retain friendly relations with the Eskimo and wherever possible to trade with them for any surplus food, blubber or oil. The Eskimo and I stood together on the deck for it was a clear day. Far away on the skyline I could clearly see the black tent we had left at Terror Bay – now fallen on the ground. Crozier had visited it and we had withheld his information about the horrible fate of the men abandoned there. I did not want the Eskimos to learn that we 'civilised' white men could resort to cannibalism, so I tried to convey to him that he should never visit that tent for there were very bad things there. I then took him down into the great cabin and gave him many presents. When he left he seemed happy enough. But I doubt that we shall see him again.

Five years in the ice on an expedition supplied for only three years, requires explaining how we last few still survive. And this by fishing from the ship in the short summer when Erebus looks like a fishing boat with fish drying on lines. More is smoked ashore in our smoke house using oak chippings. More important are the hunting skills of the four hunters who have really become Eskimos. These four are of course in the best of health as they spend a lot of time away from the ship and often live with the Eskimos. I hear our Chief Hunter Bosun Terry even has an Eskimo wife at the summer camp where our hunters join the Eskimos to go summer fishing at Lake Amitsoq.

To keep some hope alive and prevent the morale of the crew from sinking into despondency is a big part of my life today. I cannot ask these half starved men to make any big physical efforts but try to keep them occupied aboard ship. I still talk to the men about possible rescue, as I am certain the Admiralty has sent out men and ships to seek us.

Our best hope of course is that that some of the men who have left the ships may reach civilisation and get a message back to the Admiralty that Erebus, although trapped, is still occupied. We have not given up hope that some of Lieutenant Irving's party got through in summer 1848. Our second chance is that the attempt made by Lieutenant Fairholme in summer 1849 will succeed. If he got through to the whaling ships then we might yet expect an Admiralty relief expedition this coming summer of 1850. Finally there is the hope that the large party of mainly Terror men that left last month will get to whaling ships this year, 1850. If the latter succeed then a rescue attempt can be expected in summer 1851.

The brightest events in our lives are when our hunters with sledges loaded with their meat or fish return to the ship. This never fails to cheer up everyone aboard. The news they bring us is always about the Eskimos. We are always hopeful of hearing of white men looking for us, but so far the hunters questions have never told of anyone searching for us. This bothers me greatly for I am certain that the Admiralty will be making a great effort to find us.

My thoughts often stray to that time before we sailed, when we were lionised by the press. What can they be writing about us today? For them we will have vanished off the face of the earth. I don't want to go into regrets and recriminations but our failure to leave a message at Beechey Island has probably resulted in the search expeditions seeking us in too many places. We know one place for certain where they have not been because that is where we are.

How could we have once been so overconfident as to think we might be home after only one year and that leaving messages was therefore unimportant. Since entering this fearsome ice river that has trapped us, we have left many message cylinders but in places so remote that they might not be found for many years.

Everything depends now on whether the ship will be released in the summer thaw of July 1850.

CHAPTER 19

Expedition diary, written August the tenth 1850
by Bosun Thomas Terry

This is Erebus Bosun Thomas Terry, Chief Hunter of Erebus, writing in August 1850 following the death of our much respected Captain Fitzjames.

When July 1850 arrived for Erebus with her small crew of Captain Fitzjames and his fourteen 'Black Men,' I was ashore on Imnguyaaluk Island. I was leading a hunting party mainly for birds, but always in sight of the ship. The Captain had arranged to fly a large signal flag and fire the signal guns, if there was any sign of the ice breaking up. It was my job then to get everyone back to the ship as soon as possible.

The big event occurred on the twenty-eighth of July and we heard the signal cannon firing. It was the signal for us to hasten back to the ship with all speed. Getting back to the ship proved very difficult because of the many large melt-water pools lying on the surface of the sea ice. But with luck we made it before a boat had to be sent to rescue us. Open lanes were appearing at long last in the sea ice. One even passed within eighty yards of the ship.

The next three weeks were appalling hard work because we were so few. First we had to cut the ship out of the ice and get her into the open lane. Then there was the handling of the sails. With so few of us we never got a full set up at any time. We did however manage to use the steam engine and propeller three times as we worked the ship south along the leads in the ice. The further south we went the more open and more common the leads became, until finally ahead of us we could see the open water channel running along the coastline of the North American continent.

With the ship sailing slowly south west and open water visible ahead with the low land of the American continent beyond, Captain Fitzjames was in great spirits and filled with joy:

'By Jove, we have done it men,' he cried several times, 'We have done it at long last.' We all cheered and an exuberant Captain added:

'There is the sea route home.' So we cheered again.

He then shouted: 'It has taken us five years but we have made it into the summer open water channel at long last. All we have to do now is follow it to the west and emerge in Bering Strait.'

The Captain decided that a celebration was needed. The rum had been finished two years ago and we were now like the Eskimos drinking only water. The birds we had brought back on board with us did not last very long and the only supply of food on board the ship was the condemned tinned food. The Captain decided that be damned to the problems of the tinned food, but he would have himself a dish of good English beef from the tins. Most of us declined and settled for some smoked fish and a thin soup made with the last of the birds. The Captain selected a two-pound tin of beef with vegetables for his celebratory meal. It was a happy evening for we felt liberated from the ice trap at long last. We spent the evening singing songs as the ship continued to move slowly towards the south west

However next morning we were filled with fear when we

saw that Captain Fitzjames, our last surviving officer, was ill. Had the curse of the tinned food returned to haunt us? The ship moved on slowly south west and the captain's health declined. He followed all the symptoms of the others who had died of the suffocating disease. We knew that there was no cure possible. So as the captain became confined to his cabin and the coast approached, we decided to anchor the ship and see what would happen next. This was done and the sails furled. Then we waited to see if the captain would recover. The Captain's illness exactly followed the pattern we had seen with Commander Gore and Captain Crozier and many others. He died two days later.

Every man was devastated and most wept. Some were in despair for Captain Fitzjames had been a strong and determined leader who had won the respect and thanks of all those who had returned from the catastrophic 1848 retreat. He had given us hope and two more years of life. That this could happen now at the very moment of our escape from the ice and in our hour of triumph in having sailed through the North-West Passage into known waters at long last seemed so enormously unfair.

The last fourteen of us had an emergency meeting. How easily we all fitted into the great cabin of Erebus where so many other emergency meetings had been held these past three years. There was considerable debate by everyone to consider what we should do next. The first conclusion was that it seemed impossible now to sail on as we no longer had a navigator.

It was decided that we would honour our Captain by leaving his body in state in the great cabin as a sign of respect. The ship that he had fought so hard to save would become his tomb. So Captain Fitzjames' body was dressed in his now somewhat tattered best uniform (he had worn it on the 1848 retreat) and cocked hat and he was laid on the long table in the great cabin with his sword and medals. A board with his name, the date and 'R.I.P' quickly hammered out with brass tacks was placed alongside the body. The crew assembled and we held a short service for him in which his great efforts to get his crew and his ship home through the North-West Passage were remembered. He had given us all two more years of life after the 1848 retreat failed. Afterwards we sealed and locked the door, never to be opened again.

A second meeting was to be held for the next morning in the officer's wardroom to decide our next move. The men were all asked to decide what they wanted by early next morning. There was not a lot of time left of the summer thaw and a great deal needed to be done, especially hunting for a food supply and more skins to make winter clothing.

Next day I addressed the meeting with:

'Boys, the ship is now in the open-water passage along the northern margin of the American continent. This is the open-water route to Bering Strait that Captain Fitzjames wanted to sail home on. Before he died he succeeded in his ambition to get Erebus through that dreadful ice river that blocks the North-West Passage. We are the first to have sailed through the North-West Passage. But today we have no officers left to navigate the ship and it is a very long and tortuous route. I do not think that the last fourteen of us will succeed in sailing Erebus there. What is your thinking?'

The matter was discussed and almost all agreed with me. Then the Captain's Coxswain James Rigden (he was Sir John's coxswain at the start of the expedition) spoke up:

'Men I know I'm speaking not only for myself but for

others too when I say that I don't wish to face another winter in the ice with the very poor food that we have. It will probably mean eating more of the tinned food and more of us will probably die of the suffocating disease. Another ten months trapped aboard this ship will drive me crazy. The water channel to the west is open. It's where Captain Fitzjames wanted to take the ship. I'd like to take a boat and a crew and sail west immediately to make the most of the remaining summer thaw. There is no hope of reaching Bering Strait this summer, but we might get as far as the Mackenzie River and could attempt to get along it to the Great Slave Lake and the Hudson's Bay outposts there'.

This was followed by some discussion and it seemed the majority of men were in favour of making the escape attempt. I then spoke;

'I'm sorry boys, but I cannot agree to leaving by boat. I prefer to remain with the ship for two reasons. First our lives are not in danger here for we have become skilled in the Eskimo way of life and can survive by hunting all the year round. Second I believe there's a good chance that some of the men from the earlier escape attempts may have got through to civilisation. If alerted then the Admiralty will send out a relief expedition to us. Also Sir John Ross might yet find us as he told Sir John he would come looking for him if we failed to return. So if we remain here with the ship I believe there is a good chance of being rescued sometime in the next two years.'

James Rigden spoke: 'I am sorry to hear this Tom as you and your hunters would considerably increase our chances of success with your hunting skills. Nonetheless I am determined to go. So anyone wanting to come with me by boat please put up an arm.'

The show of arms indicated that ten men would leave by boat and four of us and Neptune our hunting dog would remain with the ship. James Rigden spoke again:

'We will leave this afternoon just as soon as we have a boat ready and loaded with camping and hunting gear'.

'I am sorry our food supply is so low James,' I replied. 'We have plenty of tinned food but that is all.'

'We will take some for emergencies but it is summer and the caribou and birds are plentiful, so we will live off fresh food as Captain Crozier wished in 1848'.

'Very well, James. When you leave I will cut the anchor rope and we will sail Erebus as far east as possible to put her on the shores of the Adelaide Peninsula. That way we will be very close to known good hunting grounds and the narrow sea passage where the Eskimo hunt the caribou in summer'.

'Are you sure you are not thinking of your Eskimo wife James?' he replied and the men laughed.

So the meeting broke up. Both teams now rushed about in order to take advantage of the last of the summer thaw. We four hunters assisted our colleagues with lowering a whale boat and loading her. She was soon loaded with an assortment of camping gear, guns and ammunition, clothing and bedding. Food was not abundant, but a selection of the feared tins was put aboard along with some dried fish and seal blubber. We were confident that a hunt over the Adelaide Peninsula in the next days would yield birds and deer for our small party remaining behind.

In a remarkably short time the whaler was ready to leave and hands were shaken by both parties and best wishes exchanged. The men scrambled down into the whale boat and she was cast off. Her sails were raised and off she went in the opposite direction to that which we would now take

Erebus. When they had grown small in the distance, I turned to my three colleagues and said:

'Very well, boys, let's get some sails on Erebus and cut the anchor cable. We must take the ship as close as we can to the Adelaide Peninsula and anchor her there.'

The anchor cable was soon cut with an axe and a few sails were unfurled. We turned the ship to the east. Fortunately the weather was still mild and she responded and moved slowly towards the Adelaide Peninsula. One man was taking soundings as we did not want to wreck her. A spare anchor was then spliced onto the anchor cable and we watched the coast closely for reefs. We continued to sail slowly to the east until early next morning when we found ourselves near some islands in Wilmot and Compton Bay in only ten fathoms of water. So we dropped the anchor and furled our sails. Later we put down a second anchor as this was to be the final resting place of Erebus. We had developed a great respect for the ship as she had carried us through very many adventures and crises.

As we had given the last of the fresh food to the boat crew, we needed to start hunting immediately. So we secured the ship, lowered a dinghy and filled it with camping and hunting gear and then moved ashore onto one of the small islets where we built our summer hunting camp. None of us wanted to stay aboard Erebus any more as she was full of sad memories and those much feared tins of food. Our hunting Eskimo lifestyle required us to move around and to live where the animals and fish were. We set out next to cross the Adelaide Peninsula to reach the narrows of Malervalik were the caribou cross back onto the mainland and where they can be shot in numbers. There we met many of our

Eskimo friends also awaiting the crossing of the caribou once the ice had formed.

CHAPTER 20

So we four men and the ship's dog 'Old Neptune' became the last inhabitants of Erebus. In addition to myself we were Able Seamen Charlie Best, Able Seaman George Thompson and Cabin Boy David Young, all original Erebus men like our dog. We did not live aboard her very much for our lifestyle of hunting required us to travel around after our food sources. In fact we left the ship pretty abruptly having anchored her in Wilmot and Compton Bay in summer 1850 as we had a dire need for food at that time. We had given what we had to Coxswain James Rigden and his nine-man crew in their bid to escape to the west. We took ourselves ashore and built our first summer camp on an islet nearby that we later learned from our Eskimo friends is called Ooksooseetoo. The following summer we again built our summer camp on that island.

We have waited with the ship now in the hope of rescue for two years. We do not live on the ship very much as we are often away hunting. We do spend parts of the winter aboard ship, when not away seal hunting. Then we choose to live in the now spacious crew's quarters because of the presence of the large Fraser Patent stove. Previously fuel had been short, but now that we have arrived at what is the final destination for Erebus, there is no longer a fuel shortage, for we have a great abundance of wood to burn. Many wooden items from the ship have now been broken up to heat our quarters, cook and melt snow for drinking water. Ironically we do not use the central piped water heating system as we do not need to heat the whole deck and also because the pipes are broken having frozen during one of our absences in the first winter there. We moved some furniture from the officer's area to give ourselves some comfort.

There is no advantage to us to be aboard the ship as a snow house or igloo is warmer if only heated by a blubber oil lamp. For the past two summers we have put up tents on Ooksooseetoo Island and used it as a hunting camp. We have also made a late summer journey each year to join our Eskimo friends at Lake Amitsoq in the centre of King William Island where we fish and feast with them and bring back sledge loads of frozen fish. There my Eskimo wife Yuka and others make us a new set of winter clothing from our caribou furs.

Today Cabin Boy David Young has grown into a fine young man and an excellent hunter. He is tremendously fit and can outrun everyone else. He and Old Neptune have run down many a wounded caribou and come back with the meat wrapped in the skin. He is almost an Eskimo nowadays after seven years in the Arctic and I wonder if he will ever be able to live in England again, even if he ever gets back there.

A year ago we were in our summer camp on Ooksooseetoo Island when Charlie Best cut himself while working on a piece of wood. It was a deep wound and became infected. His condition worsened despite our best efforts and he died. We buried him on the island making a nice grave for him with a wooden headboard. Ever since then we have been only three men and a dog.

We talk a lot still about possible search parties finding us. We don't know if any of the parties that left the ship got through to civilisation and alerted the Admiralty to our predicament. The general feeling was that rescue might come from Back's Great Fish River. If we are found now, then our countrymen will have difficulty recognising us, for we have become Eskimos. We dress in furs, our hair and beards are long and greasy and our skin black with blubber soot. We now speak the language of the Eskimos and live like them. We are fit and healthy and now enjoy eating raw fish and meat as well as cooked food.

We have many Eskimo friends and have camped with them. Perhaps because we are so few, these shy and friendly people, who are now familiar with 'kabloonas,' are no longer afraid of us. During our first summer stays with the Eskimo at Lake Amitsoq my friend NeeVee gave me his eldest daughter Yuka as a wife. She had worked hard on our winter clothing, chewing the furs to make them soft and comfortable to wear. But she remains behind with her people when we return to the ship and our summer camp.

We have been here for two years now. It was our hope that some of our colleagues who left the ship at different times might have reached civilisation, but there have been no rescue missions. We had hoped that Sir John Ross might arrive as he had promised Sir John Franklin that he would search for him if he did not return in three years. We also hoped that a rescue mission might descend Back's Great Fish River looking for us as Lieutenant George Back did when he set out to find Sir John Ross and the Victory expedition. We fear that the absence of search parties is because none of our men got through to civilisation. So the search parties are looking in the wrong places.

After two years of waiting, we have decided over the past winter, that rescue is not likely to come now. We don't wish to live the rest of our lives tied to Erebus as she is no longer essential to our Eskimo way of life. In fact we can live better without her so that we are free to travel around hunting.

When we returned to the ship this past autumn we were not too surprised to find that she had been broken into by the Eskimos and many things useful to them had been removed. They did not understand the locked doors and had broken through them. This has caused us to seriously rethink our situation. One evening sitting around the Fraser Patent stove with a good wood fire crackling away I raised the subject of our future:

'Boys, we have now waited two years for a rescue effort to arrive at the ship. I think that as this has not happened, it seems likely that none of the many escape bids by the officers and crew have succeeded. The distances are just too great. It's a terrible thought that not one man, not even Lieutenant Fairholme going north, the Terror men going east and Coxswain Rigden going west got home. Even Sir John Ross has failed to appear.'

This was discussed and there was general agreement that this was probably the case. So I continued:

'We now have a new problem. The Eskimo have discovered the ship and started to loot her. This is understandable as she is abandoned most of the time and there are many things aboard that are immensely valuable to them. But they are destroying and removing things useful to us as well. Someone has smashed a dinghy so we only have the one left that we use in the summer. The broken doors will allow snow to drift into the ship in winter. I am sure as the word gets out that there will be a great deal more looting. They may even burn the ship by accident. Also I don't think we should be wasting our efforts to repair the ship. Without a rescue arriving now and with the looting started there is no hope for her.'

Young David said: 'Well, we no longer need the ship. She was our base for our being rescued only. Of course she still supplies us with powder and lead shot.'

George Thompson added: 'Well I can live without her. I prefer a warm igloo in the winter to this huge gloomy and damp ship.'

'So far each summer we have met up with our friends at Lake Amitsoq,' I said. 'The women there have worked on our furs to produce our new winter clothing. We will need their efforts every year.'

David said: 'Well perhaps it's time to give up the ship and stop waiting to be rescued.'

I replied: 'I agree but we do have the resources to make our own escape bid'.

Charlie asked: 'But where will we go?'

We thought about it for a while and considered the many possibilities as they had all been tried already by groups of men from the ships who had probably paid the price of failure with their lives. So I said:

'Well we have the advantage of having learned the Eskimo way of life and their language which the others did not have. I would suggest we journey to the east as the shortest route to an area where we might find whaling ships'.

Following some general discussion it was agreed that during the summer when the caribou were abundant, we would abandon Erebus for the last time and head east in our own bid to escape. So we scoured the ship for useful things to carry on our sledge. Our main interest lay in powder and lead for our guns, but needles, fishhooks and beads which are not heavy were important as well as some knives and small axes. In May 1852 we left the ship for the last time and set out to the east heading for the Melville Peninsula.

Once there we hope to meet with whaling ships. We were no longer afraid of the winter cold for we dress like Eskimos and our Eskimo friends have taught us how to live in the winter, as they do in snow houses on the sea ice and how to hunt the bearded seal. Old Neptune has become a wonderful hunting dog and lives well on the offal of the kill.

CHAPTER 21

A pocket notebook entry for Autumn 1862 by Amaruq
the Hunter, formerly Thomas Terry, Bosun and
Chief Hunter of Erebus

In May 1852 the three of us and Old Neptune left Erebus and our summer camp on Ooksooseetoo Island for the last time and set off across the ice to the Adelaide peninsula nearby to travel east and to hunt. Before leaving the ship I entered the great cabin where Captain Fitzjames' body lay. I went through the locked doorway that the Eskimos had smashed.

The captain's body was now lying on the cabin floor, presumably moved by the Eskimos. I left it there and put the expedition's diary in a prominent place in case any rescuers arrived after we had left so that a record of the expedition might be found. We left the ship with the decks still covered in canvas from our last winter occupation.

Our journey was a long one travelling about 400 miles, first crossing the Adelaide Peninsula and then across the southern ends of Pelly and Committee Bays to Repulse Bay. Next we travelled about 250 miles along the length of the Melville Peninsula but we found no whaling ships anywhere. On our way up the Melville Peninsula, we were crossing a lake by propelling ourselves on rafts of ice. Able Seaman George Thompson lost his balance and was tipped into the water. We were unable to get to him in time and he sank with all his equipment. It was a great loss that we felt keenly for we were now reduced to only two men and Old Neptune our dog, who continues to thrive.

Eventually we camped on the north end of the Melville Peninsula and set about hunting enough caribou for our winter food supply and also a new set of skins for clothing and boots. We planned for the coming winter to go out onto the sea ice hunting seals and like the Eskimos live in igloos.

That autumn we camped near a rocky outcrop where there were many flat slabs of rock lying around. More for fun we built ourselves a very distinctive meat and fur store from these slabs. We laid them in a circle and then kept adding more but each layer was a little further back than the one underneath. The result was a sort of stone igloo or what is known in some of the Western Isles as a beehive hut, as they were built long ago by monks. David was very impressed as he had seen nothing like it before.

It was during the course of this winter (1852-53) living in an igloo of our own making that David and I had some very long discussions.

I started one off with: 'We've seen no whaling ships off the Melville Peninsula. I'm wondering if it's really worth the effort of looking for rescue. It's now almost eight years that we have lived in the Arctic. I am pretty sure we have been given up for dead back home. What do you think?'

David replied: 'I don't remember all that much about home. I was an orphan raised by an uncle and cannot remember my parents. I joined the Navy at the age of twelve years and most of my life has been here in the Arctic. I don't have any friends or family back home. How about you?'

'Oh I was married once but being away at sea most of the time put an end to that. The thought of returning home now worries me. There will be back pay outstanding from the Navy but that is all. There is no employment for a man with Eskimo skills in England. I would have to find a ship and go back to sea again. I fear if we return we will be found to be such missfits with an unbelievable story that the only way we will make a living is by being exhibited in circus shows'.

David then made a profound suggestion: 'Then why don't we stop looking for rescue and settle down here. We have the skills to provide for families and our lives could be healthy and happy. I think we would be welcomed as great hunters if we were to join any Eskimo band. You already have an Eskimo wife and I could take one too. I am sure we could live very well.'

'That's a very good suggestion. Let's think about it.'

The discussion continued through that winter. We had a long debates about the merits of returning home and found that to do so would certainly put us into poverty in England. We also found ourselves at a great disadvantage on the Melville Peninsula in having no wives there to cook, and make and repair our caribou skins clothes each winter.

So we finally came around to the idea of settling down with the Eskimos. I suggested we return the following summer to Lake Amitsoq and find our friend NeeVee and my Eskimo wife Yuka or 'Bright Star'. We did this. Our Eskimo friends were delighted with our return and became exceedingly happy when we explained that we wished to settle with them. We each took an Eskimo name. Mine, because of my grey hair, is Amaruq meaning 'Grey Wolf'. David because of his long strides and running ability became another 'Aglooka'.

This act marked the end of our old lives as stranded sailors of the Royal Navy hoping for a rescue that never came. It marked the beginning of our new lives as adopted Eskimos living with our friends and families. NeeVee in particular was so pleased that he gave his second daughter Osha, meaning 'Daughter of the Sun', to David as a wife.

Perhaps not surprisingly within a year we each had a son. From that time onwards we measured time by the ages of our sons and the seasons. We were immensely proud of our sons. Mine, because of his black hair, is called Aklaq meaning 'Black Bear'. David's son with light brown hair is called Atiqtalaaq meaning 'Polar Bear Cub'. It was not too long afterwards that we found ourselves each with a daughter. My daughter is Alasic meaning 'Alice' and David's daughter is Yura meaning 'Beautiful'. Our two sons became our pride and joy for they, like us, became great hunters.

But by that time we had exhausted our gunpowder and lead and we all hunted in the traditional Eskimo ways. Old Neptune who was very popular with the Eskimos, who had never seen such a dog, also got himself a family with several puppies that also proved good hunting dogs. There was no poverty, although sometimes the hunting failed and everyone knew hunger. But we were both happy with our new lives and families. In fact looking back we wonder why we had spent so many years hoping for rescue.

CHAPTER 22

*Inuit testimony collected by Charles Francis Hall
about the fate of Erebus*

One day an Inut of the Utjulik area was out hunting seals, when he saw a dark object far out to seaward in the ice. It was about the middle of May and close to the end of the seal hunting season. He went to investigate and found it was a great wooden ship of the kabloonas. It was sitting in smooth young ice that was only about a year old. A plank extended from the ships side down to the ice, and sweepings from the deck lay on the ice alongside. The sails and rigging were in complete order and there were four boats hanging from the sides and a small boat above the quarter deck. All the doors and hatches were closed and locked. The deck was completely encased in canvas as was done for winter. The Inut was afraid but went aboard and found a knife. He ran back to where the Inuit were camping and showed it to them. Then all of the men decided to go to the ship.

When they got aboard the ship they first checked to see if anyone was living there but found no-one. One man seeing a small boat hanging from the stern wanted it for a meat trough and cut the ropes. It fell onto the ice on one end and was smashed. The others, in order to get inside the ship, broken a hole through a locked door. Inside in a big cabin they found the body of a large kabloona with long teeth. He was dead but all his clothes were on. It took five Inuit to lift him as he was very heavy, so they left him there. There was a bad smell in that room. They entered a very big room that was dark and they had to feel around and found there many useful things. There were many good buckets, boxes, guns and tins of meat. The meat was fat like pemmican and good to eat. The Inuit took only things useful to them, including knives, forks, spoons, pans and cups.

A little while later the fresh footprints of four men and a dog were found on an islet nearby. Some had seen the footprints of John Ross near his ship Victory as well as those of John Rae and knew these to be the footprints of Kabloonas. Such footprints are long and narrow in the middle, like the boots the kabloonas wear. One of the men had very long footsteps and was evidently a great runner. The Inuit followed the footprints for a long way and found where the kabloonas had killed and eaten a young deer.

From time to time the Inuit would visit the ship to take out useful things especially iron and wood. Eventually the ship drifted ashore onto an islet where one end became submerged. The other end of the ship was heavily salvaged for wood and iron by the Inuit for many years, until little remained. Many books were seen but not taken by the Inuit for whom they had no value.

Later the Inuit were visited by Captain McClintock (in 1859) who was told about the wreck and who purchased many things taken from her. He was very interested to purchase any of the officers' silver cutlery and plate.

Then soon afterwards the ship was rafted offshore by the ice, where she sank and only her masts showed above the water. The wreck was much broken up by the ice and then the masts, timbers, boxes and casks drifted ashore. The place where she sank was near O'Reilly Island, a little to the east of the north end of this island, between it and Wilmot and Compton Bay.

CHAPTER 23

Inuit testimony

After the kabloonas sailed their big ship away to the south from Imnguyaaluk Island things were quiet. Then one day some years later two brothers were out hunting seals near Cape Crozier, the westernmost cape on King William Island. It was the spring, at the time when the snow melts about the seal's breathing holes. They saw a dark mass far out in the sea ice and looking carefully saw that it was a big ship of the kabloonas. They ran to their camp site and told all the Inuit. Next day all the men went out to the ship. They found the ship was deserted and so they decided to take things from her that were useful to them. But these Inuit had never met kabloonas and did not know the use of many of the things they found.

At first they were afraid to go down inside the ship, but after a while they grew bolder and ventured inside. Here they found many dead men, all lying in the sleeping places. They could see that the men had all died of a sickness. They then entered the great dark room in the middle of the ship. Here they found many useful things, much wood and iron. They found guns but not knowing the use of them, broke them up to use the metal pieces for harpoon heads, knives and tools. They also found percussion caps which they thought were thimbles used by dwarfs amongst the crew of the ship. They also found tins of meat which they opened and ate. Many became ill and later died.

Because it was dark in the big room, they took tools to cut a window through the side of the ship to let in the light. But they cut too low, below the water line. Soon the ship filled with water and sank taking with her many things valuable to the Inuit.

CHAPTER 24

Pocket Notebook entry for Spring 1869 by Amaruq the hunter, formerly Thomas Terry Chief Hunter and Bosun of H.M.S. Erebus.

It came as a great surprise to me that I should ever write again in my small pocket notebook and this after such a great length of time has passed since the loss of the great Admiralty expedition of Sir John Franklin. David and I had long been settled with the Eskimos and both of us had taken wives and now have families. We lived as Eskimos and daily speak their language and hunt with them. Our guns brought prosperity to our small group. David and I had the reputation of great hunters. When the day came when there was no more powder and shot, we continued hunting using the traditional Eskimo methods. David in particular became a hunter of great fame. We were both immensely proud of our two sons, both now aged fourteen years. With them we formed a team of proficient hunters and enjoyed the competition with the other Eskimo hunters for food. Our wives and daughters brightened our lives considerably with their cheerful friendly approach to life and yet at the same time did the vast amount of work expected of Eskimo women especially making our new fur clothing each winter and cooking and raising our children

We had now lived as Eskimos for fifteen years and our responsibilities and thoughts were entirely for our families and our community. We thought in the Eskimo language, we no longer used the Christian calendar but used only the season and the ages of our sons to mark the passage of time. It is a rich life amidst the icy spendours of a vast and empty world that we had come to love and accept as our own. I suppose it would be true to say that we were now through and through Eskimos.

One day our simple happy world was disturbed when some visiting Eskimos talked of a big kabloona who had come into our area and was asking many questions about the lost expedition and of two kabloonas whose route he was following along the Melville Peninsula. Although twenty four years had now elapsed since the great Franklin expedition had sailed and fifteen years since David and I had settled down with the Eskimoes, it seem obvious that this stranger was seeking David and myself.

So I took David aside and together we took a walk outside our summer camp for a private conversation. I opened it with:

'David, a group of visiting Eskimos are talking of a kabloona who is in the area. He's asking about the lost expedition and two kabloonas who passed this way years ago. I think he's looking for us both. But he's travelling alone with a small group of Eskimos, so it cannot be an Admiralty search expedition.'

David frowned: 'Well we waited eight years without rescue and now is not the time. We are Eskimos now, we have our families to look after, and we are a crucial part of our small community. I cannot leave my family now. We both have sons fourteen years old and about to become men. I want to be with my family now and see my son and daughter grow and have their own families'.

I mulled this over: 'Agreed. I hear he has an Eskimo couple with him who he has taken back to the west and exhibited in shows. Maybe he wants to do the same with us. Put us in a circus freak show and charge a penny a time for people to come and look sat us – 'Come and see the British Royal Navy Seamen who became Eskimos'.

David said worriedly: 'You mean he would make money and our families would starve in our absence. Or perhaps put our families on show with us. No thank you'.

'That is not all that concerns me,' I replied. 'I served many years in the Royal Navy before we sailed with Sir John. There I saw a lot of trouble made for men who lost ships and equipment. It is a court martial offence to lose a ship. If we reappear back in England there would have to be a lot of enquiries by the admiralty. An awful lot of very expensive equipment was lost. Somebody has to be responsible for that. Also a lot of very fine men died and no doubt their families will want to know the details of what happened to them. Our lives could become miserable facing many investigations into everything that went wrong.'

'I think we must protect our families first,' David insisted. 'It is important that we do not meet this man and that he does not know we exist. In order to preserve our families and community we have to be dead, so we can be left in peace.'

'Perhaps it's time to take our small group and make a long hunting trip,' I said thoughtfully. 'We should take all the dogs as some of them look most unlike the Eskimo breed. There is a lot of Old Nep. in some of his children.'

'David added: 'I'll go and see the shaman and tell him the kabloona might be a bad spirit and we are going hunting to be away from him. We can ask him to make some magic so that nobody will speak of us if the Kabloona comes here.'

'A good idea let's do it'.

So we moved away from the Kabloona and hunted new areas for a year, until we heard that he had left the area. We had no wish to disrupt our peaceful simple way of life. We did not want to become oddities in the eyes of our wives, children and community. Nor did we want our families exhibited in a circus. We preferred to forget all about the disaster of the Franklin expedition and the many unhappy memories of the suffering and loss of good men and friends. We no longer talk about the expedition and both firmly believe that western people would probably not believe us if we told our story.

Then one day with our families, we returned to our old area and met up again with our friends and relations. The old shaman in particular was very pleased to see us and explained how he had used strong magic to protect us from the kabloona. He told us that he had forbidden all the Eskimos to speak our names or the names of our wives and children on penalty of contracting a very painful illness that would result in a slow death. It had worked wonderfully well. The kabloona had learned some tales of our passage up the Melville Peninsula. But once we had settled down and become Eskimos with new names and families, everything was forbidden and he learned nothing about our lives and the lives of our families. We were immensely grateful and promised the shaman a lifetime supply of hunting delicacies and much meat. This delighted him.

So by means of some trickery by the shaman of our group, our way of life and our families were protected from the world we had once known. We can now continue to live a simple healthy life in peace. Our sons will become men and like us will be great hunters. Our sons and daughters will marry and have children. David and I will continue to enjoy the hunt and the socialising in the big winter igloos and the summer caribou hunting and the fishing camps. Sometimes we listen silently and sadly to tales told of the great ships that came one time and were lost with many kabloonas in the ice.

David was only a twelve-year-old boy when the great expedition sailed and his life today is very different to what it would have been in England that he no longer thinks of as 'the old world'. However I lived and had a life back in England and sailed aboard the Admiralty ships for many years before joining the great expedition. Sometimes at night I lie awake thinking about that past life. I wonder how it is possible that such a great expedition of two great ships could have been lost and that the admiralty failed to find us. I wonder that so many gallant men and officers died because the ships were trapped in the ice and nobody ever came to find us. Sometimes I wonder did we really travel so far that we came to a place on earth that is beyond the reach of modern man with his many new inventions and machines? At other times I wonder if God spared David and I, from amongst so many fine courageous men, to show us a better simpler way of life without the crowding and poverty of the old world we have lost. Either way I give thanks that we were spared from so many to find new lives and happiness with our families in this empty strikingly-beautiful great wilderness unchanged since it was made by the hands of God.

THE END

HISTORICAL NOTES

This novel is my best understanding of what probably happened to the lost Arctic expedition of Sir John Franklin that set out in 1845. The evidence on which each of the chapters is based is presented separately in an academic volume titled *Franklin's Fate*, yet to be published. In it all available evidence is described, being Inuit testimony, relics found by searchers, modern forensic investigations on remains, and, of course, the as yet incomplete data on the locations, condition and contents of the two ships found only in 2014 and 2016. The data in the unpublished review has been grouped into chapters that each build a step in the history of the lost expedition. The present volume presents the story of the lost expedition without going back to the numerous data sources that are given fully in the above mentioned unpublished review.

There is a vast amount of literature on the lost Franklin expedition that continues to appear today due to the interest generated by the use of the internet and the modern Canadian government backed searches of land and sea. Scattered throughout the literature are fragments of information about the lost expedition. It is a like a vast jigsaw puzzle and has entertained numerous enthusiastic followers of the lost expedition.

My own interest started when I was an undergraduate at London University in 1963 when a friend (the late Dr. Alan Date) gave me a copy of McClintock's *Voyage of the Fox*. The questions raised by this book have puzzled me throughout my life. So wanting to have some better information on what probably happened I made this project my first job on retiring as a geologist. Reading the literature is today fairly straightforward with the internet and Amazon.com. Having computers to write with enables one to assemble a vast number of fragments and then rearrange them into an order to get a probable story.

There are a number of decisions to be made. The Victorian contemporaries of Sir John Frankin were appalled at Inuit reports of cannibalism. Victorian society refused to accept the Inuit testimony, instead blaming the cannibalism on the Inuit. Times have changed considerably and today the Inuit testimony can be seen as simple observations by an innocent people often of things they did not understand. I have included all the Inuit testimony that I can find. Only one problem arose and that is that there are three different testimonies of the sinking of three ships. One is not needed. Based on the new information of the state of the two sunken expedition ships found in 2014 and 2016, I have rejected the testimony of Kokleearngnun and retained the other two.

Writing the story as a novel has given me the leeway to fill in gaps in the record. For example, in chapter 7 dealing with the ice pressures on the two trapped ships is taken from Sir Ernest Shackleton's 1915 experience, when he lost his ship 'Endurance' in the moving ice of the Weddell Sea off Antarctica.

Inuit testimony from Spring 1849 (the Chieftain Report) indicates that the one ship was still lying on her beam ends at that time. More Inuit testimony describes finding a ship with many bodies in bunks inside. This suggests that the ship was used during one winter as a mausoleum ship for those who died in the time of darkness when the land and sea were hard frozen.

In this novel, the suffocating disease that ravages the expedition (chapters 6 and 9) is not scurvy nor lead poisoning (although these were present) but botulism carried in some of the 9,500 tins of preserved meats, vegetables and soups hastily prepared at the last minute by Stephen Goldner. This possibility was identified by Scott Cookman in his book 'Ice Blink' (2000).

Chapter 15 is suggested by common sense plus the discovery of the 1993 private 'Lady Franklin Memorial Expedition' with Peter Wadhams, Maria Pia Casarini and Wayne Davidson of the remains of what appeared to be a 'Franklin era' whaleboat at Back Bay on Prince of Wales Island about a half way to Lancaster Sound.

The events on the Todd Islets (chapter 17) are based on Inuit testimony of five undisturbed bodies found together near the top of one of the Todd islets. The older leader with the distinctive grey beard and whiskers was lying with his telescope, shot gun and a tin of pemmican. The Inuit opened the tin and ate the contents with relish and no ill effects.

Also in chapter 17, Lieutenant Hodgson is paying the price of an earlier hostile encounter. The Inuit at the mouth of Back's Great Fish River were friendly to George Back and his expedition when they descended and ascended the river in 1834. On the return trip, unknown to George Back, some of his men surprised some of the Inuit men who shot arrows at them, Back's men fired back killing three and possibly wounding others. They did not tell Back about this until they returned to England, so Back was unable to smooth things out.

Identification of a Royal Marine Sergeant (chapter 17) who almost reached Fort Churchill is based on the identification of what was probably his sword as being British Infantry rather than Royal Navy - an excellent piece of detective work by Russell Potter (2000).

A new interpretation is presented of the famous Inuit testimony of the 'Black Men' - an Inut visit to a ship with one officer and a small crew of black thin men in sight of the tent at Terror Bay (Chapter 18). This has previously been interpreted as a visit during a Guy Fawkes celebration with a crew with blackened faces (e.g. Potter, 2000). Here it is seen as a late visit to Erebus with her last survivors living by hunting and using seal blubber lamps in circumstances similar to those of Shackleton's men on Elephant Island.

Chapter 19 is based on many rumours from the vicinity of the Mackenzie River of white men being seen in the area. But no survivors ever arrived at the Hudson's Bay trading posts on the Great Slave Lake.

Chapter 24 with the last two survivors is a pure imaginative reconstruction as what happened to them remain unknown to this day. However, the visitor who in 1868 searched the Melville Peninsula looking for the two 'kablooknas' and their dog was Charles Francis Hall. He was an American publisher of a small newspaper in Cincinnati who became interested in the many searches for the missing Franklin expedition. He was neither a traveller nor an explorer and had a wife and children. One day he realised that God was asking him to go north and find the last survivors of the Franklin expedition. In 1860 he set out on a free passage on a whaling ship. His means were modest and ice conditions resulted in him being dropped not in the Franklin search area, but on the coast of Baffin Island. There by good fortune he met an Eskimo couple Tookoolitoo (whom the whalers called 'Hannah') and Ebiering (called 'Joe'). They would be Hall's companions for the next decade.

Joe and Hannah had already been to England and been exhibited at Hull and London, where they had been taken to meet Queen Victoria. Hannah was an excellent interpreter and Joe was a guide and hunter. Hall and his two Inuit companions and their young son Terralikitaq, returned to the USA in 1863 bearing relics of the Frobisher expedition of some 300 years earlier. Hall rented out the Inuit to Barnum's Museum and took them on a fund raising lecture tour of the eastern seaboard. Terralikitaq became ill and died. The American Civil war (1861 to 1865) broke out and put an end to immediate funding for another Franklin search expedition.

But Hall and his Inuit did return to the Arctic in 1864 and spent another five years there gathering much Inuit testimony about the lost expedition and purchasing relics. Hearing of survivors on the Melville Peninsula (some reports as late as 1864), Hall took his group there in 1868, some twenty three years after the Franklin Expedition had sailed. He collected eye-witness accounts of strangers with rifles and a dog, but his search was unsuccessful.

The roles assigned to various members of the Franklin expedition in this novel are fictional.

The re-evaluation of Inuit testimony was very much the work of David Woodman in two excellent books. His work led to the discovery of the wreck of H.M.S.Erebus. I greatly enjoyed John Wilson's fictional account of the expedition but it raised the question of what really happened. On retiring as a geologist I decided, as the prime objective of my retirement, to apply myself to the project of trying to understand what really happened to the Franklin expedition.

Dr John Roobol

October 2018

SUGGESTED FURTHER READING

Amundsen, R. and Hansen, G., 1908, The North West Passage – Being a record of a voyage of exploration of the ship Gjoa 1903-1907, vol. 2. Reprinted 2014, Cambridge University Press.

Battersby, William, 2010, James Fitzjames: the mystery Man of the Franklin Expedition: The History Press Co., and Dundum Press, Canada, 224 p.

Beattie O., and Geiger, J., 1987, Frozen in time: Unlocking the Secrets of the Franklin Expedition: Western Producer Prairie Books, Saskatoon, Saskatchewan.

Cookman, Scott, 2000, Ice Blink – The tragic fate of Sir John Franklin's lost Polar expedition: John Wiley and Sons, New York, 244p.

Cyriax, R.J., 1939, Sir John Franklin's Last Arctic Expedition: Methuen and Company, London. Reprinted 1977, The Arctic Press, Plaistow and Sutton Coldfield, 222p.

Eber, D.H., 2008, Encounters on the passage: Inuit meet the explorers. University of Toronto Press, 168 p.

Fitzjames, J., 1852, Journal of James Fitzjames aboard Erebus, 1845: Nautical Magazine and Chronicle, 21, p.158 – 165, p. 195 – 201. Also: Mangles, J. (Ed.), 1852, Papers and Despatches relating to the Arctic searching expeditions of 1850-51-52. 2nd Edition, Francis and John Rivington, London, p.76 – 88.

Gilder, W. H., 1899, The Search for Franklin, A Narrative of the American Expedition under Lieutenant Schwatka: Nelson and Sons, Reprinted 2014, Cambridge University Press.

Gould, R.T., 1927, Admiralty Chart 5101, Chart showing the vicinity of King William Island, with the various positions in which relics of the Arctic Expedition under Sir John Franklin have been found. Compiled by Lieut. Commdr. R.T. Gould.

Keenleyside, A., Bertulli, M., and Fricke, H.C., 1997, The final days of the Franklin expedition: new skeletal evidence: Arctic. vol. 50, no.1, (March 1997), p.36-46.

McGoogan, K., 2001, Fatal Passage. Harper Collins Publishers, Canada; Bantam Edition, 2002, 328p.

McGoogan, K., 2005, Lady Jane's Revenge: Harper Collins, Toronto, 468 p.

M'Clintock, Captain, F.L. 1859, The Voyage of the 'Fox' in the Arctic Seas - A Narrative of the Discovery of the fate of Sir John Franklin and his companions. John Murray, Albemarle Street, London. Reprinted 2005, Elibron Classics Series, Adamant Media Corporation, 403p. Reprinted 2012, Cambridge University Press.

Nourse, J.E., Ed., 1879, Narrative of the Second Arctic Expedition Commanded by Charles Francis Hall: Washington, Government Printing Office, 778p. Reprinted by Nabu Public Domain Reprints. Lightning Source UK Ltd., Milton Keynes, UK.

Potter, R.A., 2016, Finding Franklin – The untold story of a

165-year search: McGill-Queens University Press, Canada, 262 p.

Rasmussen,K., 1931, The Netsilik Eskimos, Social Life and Spiritual Culture. Reprinted 1976 AMS Press, New York.

Ross, Sir John, 1835, Narrative of a second voyage in search of a North-west passage: and a residence in the Arctic regions during the years 1829, 1830, 1831, 1832 1833, including the report of Commander, now Captain, James Clark Ross, R.N., F.R.S., F.L.S, &c. and the discovery of the Northern Magnetic Pole; 2 volumes, Webster, Regent Street, London. Reprinted 2012, Cambridge University Press.

Smith, M., 2006, Captain Francis Crozier - Last man standing? The Collins Press, Cork, 242 p.

Stenton, D.R., 2014, "A most inhospitable coast": The report of Lieutenant William Hobson's 1859 search for the Franklin expedition on King William Island. Arctic, v. 67, No.4, p. 511-522.

Stenton, D.R., Keenleyside, A., and Park, R.W., 2015, 'The Boat Place'Burial: New Skeletal Evidence from the 1845 Franklin Expedition: Arctic, 68, no.1, p. 32-44.

Stenton, D.R., Keenleyside, A., Trepkov, D.P., and Park, R.W., 2016, Faces from the Franklin expedition? Craniofacial reconstructions of two members of the 1845 North-West Passage Expedition: Polar Record, v. 52, No. 1, p 76-81.

Wilson, J., 2000, North with Franklin: Fitzhenry & Whiteside, USA and Ontario, 305 p.

Wilson, J., 2001, John Franklin, Traveller of Undiscovered Seas: XYZ Publishing , Montreal, Canada, 175 p.

Woodman, D. C.,1991, Unravelling the Franklin Mystery –
Inuit Testimony: McGill-Queens University Press, Montreal
& Kingston, London, Buffalo, 390 p.

Woodman, D. C., 1995, Strangers among us: McGill-
Queen's University Press, Montreal & Kingston, London,
Buffalo, 166 p.

INTERNET WEBSITES:

Potter, Russell: www.ric.edu/faculty/rpotter/SJFranklin.
html

ACKNOWLEDGEMENTS

The work was made possible by the internet where many obscure and out of print books are available. Amazon.co.uk also provided an excellent rapid book service. Blogspots by Russell Potter, William Battersby and Peter Carney were helpful. The work of David Woodman was particularly valuable especially additional information that he obtained from the unpublished notebooks of C.F. Hall. The work of Dorothy Harley Eber provided critical information for the later events of the expedition. Professor Russell Potter's 2000 publication provided vital information on the grave found by Su-pung-er and his uncle in the 1860s. My thanks to my wife, Dr. Anne Roobol, for help in obtaining some books and scientific papers. My thanks to publisher Mr. James Essinger for enthusiastic support and for insisting on the dialog.